THE EXCITEMENT OF SCIENCE

THE EXCITE

BY JOHN RADER PLATT

MENT OF SCIENCE

HOUGHTON MIFFLIN COMPANY BOSTON

THE RIVERSIDE PRESS CAMBRIDGE

1962

Portions of this book have previously appeared in various magazines. Excerpts from Chapter 1, "The Excitement of Science," have been published in *Saturday Review, Air Force Magazine and Space Digest,* and *Trustee,* a publication of the American Hospital Association. This chapter also appeared in *Public Health Reports,* issued by the United States Department of Health, Education and Welfare. Chapter 2, "Style in Science," first appeared in *Harper's Magazine* for October 1956: copyright © 1956 by Harper & Brothers. Chapter 3, "Competition in Creation," is reprinted with permission from the February 1959 issue of the *Bulletin of the Atomic Scientists,* 935 East 60th Street, Chicago 37, Illinois. Chapter 4, "How Far Can We Foresee?," was originally published in the *New Republic* for December 8, 1958, under the title "Can We Foresee the Future?": copyright © 1958 by Harrison-Blaine, Inc. *Horizon* first published Chapter 5, "The Fifth Need: Novelty," in July 1959, under the title "The Fifth Need of Man": © 1959 by American Horizon, Inc.

CONTENTS

INTRODUCTION

SCIENCE is a social creation as well as an individual creation. But once created it reacts on society and changes it. Sometimes it produces those great improvements in our way of life that we all want for ourselves. Sometimes it produces grave dangers and dislocations that can be the despair of military men as well as moralists. This book is a series of reflections on these interactions between science and society.

My purpose here has been to go beyond facts as such and to begin to examine some deeper and more permanent questions about the fundamental relations between science and technology and the intellect of man which creates them; about their relations to the purposes of society which they serve or ought to serve. I discuss science as a communal enterprise; how it is related to the individual qualities of response, interpretation, decision and intelligence in the mind of man, and how these qualities may be amplified and focused more effectively than we have ever done before.

We are not in the grip of incomprehensible forces. The mind of man can determine the quality of the life of man, not by mystical but by operational methods. And today we live in a time when self-directing man, knowing and acting, can at last begin to use his highest intelligence to take responsible charge of his destiny.

It will be apparent that I am an optimist. Those who are not, who feel that we are doomed and powerless before the great forces that we have unleashed in the world or that we have discovered in ourselves, will doubtless be able to raise telling objections on every page. But I have no apologies; I am describing the situation of creative mind as I see it, from the point of view of modern physics and biology and still more from the point of view of a sanguine human being.

THE EXCITEMENT OF SCIENCE

1. THE EXCITEMENT
OF SCIENCE

I want to begin by discussing some general aspects of science today and by pointing out three particular qualities of basic science — not technology but basic science — that grow out of its communal nature and that consequently can be understood and appreciated by every social being, layman or not. They are qualities that I wish every citizen in a scientific society could be shown over and over until he begins to feel them for himself. The first quality is the excitement of science, the second is the sweep of science, and the third is the incompleteness of science.

EXCITEMENT

To say that basic science is exciting may sound like a contradiction. We are used to the really spectacular excitements of the engineers with their radar and rockets; and the life-and-death excitements of the doctors, the biological engineers, in their white coats. By contrast, the intellectual excitement of a man sitting over a microscope in a university basement tracking down a clue may seem pretty tame. But I would remind you that there are two intellectual excitements that are not tame at all and that we remember all our lives. One is the thrill of following out a chain of reasoning for yourself; the other is the pleasure of watching several strongly individualistic personalities argue about their deepest convictions. That is to say, the thrill of a detective story and the pleasure of watching a play by George Bernard Shaw. I would claim these are exactly the excitements basic science has to offer.

Moreover these intellectual thrills in science are not something distant or alien, but something closely continuous with our everyday thinking. It is true that science is complex. This is because so many men have been building it up for so long. Nevertheless every individual step in it is a little inference as simple as looking out at the weather and deciding whether or not to take a raincoat. When we look at a celebrated rocket engineer like Werner von Braun, we see a man running a big complex organization and dealing with incredible horsepower. But when we look at a basic natural scientist like James Van Allen, the university professor whose tiny satellite equipment detected radiation belts around the earth, fundamentally what we see is a man stepping to the door of his planet to see how the temperature is outside.

What is essential in any scientific development is the little chain of everyday inference, the reasoning. It may surprise many people to know that the chain of new scientific reasoning in a whole research study is frequently less complex than an everyday business decision or a crossword puzzle or a game of chess. It would have a salutary effect on our attitudes if for twenty-four hours we could cross out the words "science" and "scientist" wherever they appear, and put in their place the words "man reasoning." Even in the mathematical sciences, like physics, it is the reasoning that comes first, the equations second; and the equations will not save the theory if the reasoning is wrong. It cannot be said too often that science is not mathematics, but reasoning; not equipment, but inquiry.

The master at demonstrating reasoning to a mass audience was Conan Doyle. It would not be far wrong to think of every science story as his kind of detective story, with its puzzles and its suspense, its false leads and frayed tempers, and its brilliant Sherlock Holmeses, its half-brilliant Inspector Lestrades, and its admiring Doctor Watsons. It is interesting to remember that Galileo himself used a very similar group of characters to explain his reasoning to a mass audience. Science is the greatest of all detective stories, a continued yarn that holds its audience for life, with the disagreements of the characters nowadays just as conspicuous and as amusing as ever.

The second excitement in science, to me, is the excitement of personalities. Biography and belles-lettres have hardly touched the field of science. There is valuable literary work to be done here. We need a good biography of G. N. Lewis, whose department at Berkeley turned out half of the best physical chemists in America. We need one of William Moffitt, the witty and brilliant theoretical chemist at Harvard, whose death in 1958 at thirty-three was a loss far greater than the loss of any headlined baseball player or movie star. We need to put our senior teachers, James Franck of Chicago and Joel Hildebrand of California, and Percy Bridgman of Harvard, on Caedmon records, like poets, for posterity. There are many stories to be found in the sequences of brilliant teachers and brilliant pupils; my colleagues and I are fond of pointing out that three recent Nobel prize winners in physics got their Ph.D.'s with Fermi in our Department of Physics at the University of Chicago.

There is more unusual material, too, such as the story of the Hungarian-American scientists so brilliant that the others call them the "men from Mars." Or the story of such a man as Leo Szilard, a strange and contradictory thinker, who has surely influenced history by his unique role in starting the atomic bomb project as well as by his pioneer landmark papers in a dozen fields. The lighter material would include the amusing yarns that all scientists know about the hobbies of their favorite personalities. There are the mountain climbers; and Luis Alvarez's parlor tricks; Richard Feynman's lockpicking; Arthur Roberts' musical compositions; and the insults, and the jokes — like the story of the Hungarian who had a sign over his desk that said "Being Hungarian is not enough."

And there is excitement not only in present personalities, but in future ones, in the men who may get the Nobel prizes next year, and the year after.

When the stories of these personalities in science begin to be told, I suspect that we will find that all the men have one common characteristic: they are having fun. And the fun will be contagious. It has been said that the only people who get paid for doing exactly what they like are physicists and baseball players. When the word leaks out to the children, there will not be laboratories enough to hold the budding scientists.

SWEEP

The second quality I wish we could get across to every citizen is the scope or sweep of science. By this I mean the great range of problems covered, the range of the methods of work, and the wide range of the implications. For illustration I could select three areas which show very different patterns of development today. One of these is biophysics, the second is what is called molecular biology, and the third is some of the recent work on evolution.

Biophysics is one of the border areas of physics. It is one of the active fronts that have radiated out from the atomic physics of thirty years ago. In one direction these fronts include the new and rich and spectacular sciences of space physics, nuclear physics, and solid state physics. In the other direction, the activity runs instead along several of the borderlines with the older disciplines, giving us the somewhat quieter fields of chemical physics, biophysics, and psychophysics, all of them largely confined to the university laboratories.

These latter areas are not sharply separated. I started out two decades ago in chemical physics, studying the light absorption of dyes and similar molecules. I found that this led me to a study of chlorophyll, which was a biological molecule and therefore biophysics. And then it led me to a study of the visual pigments of the human eye, which are the first elements struck by light in the psychological act of vision, and therefore psychophysics.

Biophysics proper is not what I call an exploding field at present but one that is just simmering along nicely. An important area of study lately has been the transfer of light energy between neighboring biological molecules. Many workers feel that such a transfer might be the first step in vision and the first step in photosynthesis, as well as the first step in the damaging of tissue cells by nuclear radiation. This makes it a hot subject and numerous international conferences on it are being held. My only regret is that some people have chosen to call the subject "bioenergetics," which makes it sound more like a branch of naturopathy than a field of science.

Although the subject of energy transfer is of wide interest, the actual results are rather tenuous, partly because the experimental work has to be exceedingly painstaking. During a summing up session at a Brookhaven conference on this subject recently, the participants listed roughly a dozen new physical instruments and tools that they wished could be invented in order to facilitate work in this field. For example, methods are needed that would permit us to observe or infer the first chemical reaction steps of many biologically important molecules, including the primary molecules in vision, in photochemistry, in genetics, and the antibodies. Conceivably such methods of observation will evolve out of the fluorescence-interaction methods of Michael Kasha, or the tracer technique of Melvin Calvin, or the recent ingenious substitution technique of Engleberger and the Koshlands, or out of a completely new approach. The question remains open. Work is in progress.

Biophysics merges into a closely related area that today is anything but placid, the area of molecular biology. It has had an explosive development in the last ten years. It was notable first for the numbers of physicists, chemists, and doctors attracted into it by such inspiring microbiologists as Salvador Luria and Max Delbrück. Now it is the scene of some of the most recent Nobel prizes in medicine, the one to Joshua Lederberg, George Beadle, and Edward Tatum, and one to Severo Ochoa and Arthur Kornberg. And sitting at conferences, one watches with pleasure and astonishment the beautiful demonstrations of the other theorists and experimenters, wondering which of them will be next to get the prize.

Will it be James Watson and F. H. C. Crick, with their two-strand model of the DNA molecule so thoroughly proved in the last few years? Will it be Meselson and Stahl, or Taylor, Woods, and Hughes, with their beautiful tracer methods of testing the model? Will it be Seymour

Benzer, with his analysis of microgenetic characters a thousand times finer than any ever examined before? Will it be Fraenkel-Conrat or Cy Levinthal or some of their many competitors, racing to see who can crack the great cryptogram, the code that translates the DNA molecule into the other cell materials? Or Theodore Puck, with his method of culturing perfect tissue cells? Or Albert Coons, with his fluorescent method of labeling antibodies?

The shrewdness of such men in reasoning and experiment has brought a new atmosphere to biology. Needless to say, the older scientists are not entirely sympathetic. Oversimplification, they snort. One eminent gentleman said, and I quote: "You know there are scientists, and there are people in science who are not doing science at all. We need their auxiliary work — they build apparatus, they make minor studies — but they are not scientists."

To which the young microbiologist replies: "Well, there are two kinds of biologists, those who are looking to see if there is one thing that can be understood, and those who keep saying it is very complicated and that nothing can be understood."

Sixty years ago when Pasteur was also trying to see if there was one thing that could be understood, the audience hung breathless on his results. I think this could happen again today. At any rate, molecular biology is, next to nuclear physics, the most intellectually exciting field for a young person to enter at the present time.

A third area, still more biological, is that of the recent work on evolution discussed at the Darwin Centennial Celebration in 1959 at the University of Chicago. This celebration honored the 100th anniversary of publication of *The Origin of Species*. Several of the papers offered dramatic new illustrations of the Darwinian principle of evolution. One of these by Nicholas Tinbergen demonstrated that it is not just bones and muscles that evolve but also behavior, and he gave numerous examples of such evolution as found in the behavior of birds that nest in cramped and dangerous places.

In another paper, F. Clark Howell and Sherwood Washburn showed from the study of old skulls that man's brain has increased in size rapidly since he began using tools and fire, and is now almost three times as large as it was then. Another study, by Cesare Emiliani, showed that this evolution of our brains may have taken a time much shorter than anyone has supposed, only a few hundred thousand years according to new geological dates. In short, intelligent man, as we know him, may have developed with dramatic suddenness as a result of using his hands to manipulate the world around him. Perhaps we are still developing at the same remarkable rate. It was better brains that determined which of the man-creatures would survive then; and it is better brains that will help us to survive now, we hope.

At the Darwin conference there was also much said about man's population problem today, which is a terribly timely aspect of evolution. There was something like a three-cornered debate on population, between the grandson of the founder of evolution, Sir Charles Darwin; the biologist, Sir Julian Huxley; and another Nobel prize winner, H. J. Muller. Darwin says that in fifty to one hundred years the overcrowding of our increased population will destroy our civilization forever, and cannot be reversed, because people and groups who want to have many children will go on having them, whether it is good for the whole community or not. Huxley is more optimistic and thinks the population explosion can be stopped if we are intelligent enough to find incentives for stopping it. And Muller says that it is already urgent for us to take really dramatic steps, that is, to begin selective breeding, if we want civilization as we know it to continue.

All three men are united as scientists in saying that we are doomed if we do nothing to reduce our birth rates; they differ only in how much they think, as hopeful men, that we can do nationally and internationally about the problem. Many people may not approve of scientists offering to give their scientific knowledge and counsel to human affairs in this way, just as many people did not approve of the theory of evolution itself a century ago. But I think that the reporters who have the courage to try to transmit this population debate to the public in a full and fair way are finding that the story is as exciting, as controversial, and finally as important to history, as the debate over evolution itself ever was.

INCOMPLETENESS

Every intelligent layman should also know about a third quality, the incompleteness of science.

All science has gaps in it. The most familiar are the inevitable small gaps, the data that one could still go on taking, the unexamined minor assumptions, or the unresolved questions. Most of these do not bother us because we realize that a scientific age is an age of tentative conclusions and working rules that may well have to be changed later. Yet it is important for us to emphasize this incompleteness, especially to the young, because they have hopes and aspirations and they want an open-ended story, with something left for them to do when they finally take our places.

What is not so often realized is that science is incomplete in more serious ways, with gaps that scientists themselves, tied to their own narrow specialties, hardly realize the existence of. In some ways, for all its diversity, science is narrower now than it has ever been before. Few of the men who work on photosynthesis know anything about physics; few of the men who work on nervous tissue know any organic chemistry; few of the men who work on the brain have any understanding of the mind. There are exceptions. An Enrico Fermi or Edward Teller or Harold Urey can work on stars or nuclei or molecules, just as his fancy strikes him. A John von Neumann can work on quantum mechanics as well as the theory of games. A Percy Bridgman can work on solids as well as logic. But for every such man, there are hundreds who spend their lives repeating the kind of experiments they did for their doctor's degree.

Even the intellectual leaders are blind to some fields. For over a century, some of the greatest physicists, Young and Maxwell and Helmholtz and Schrödinger, thought it of the greatest importance to study human visual perception. To-day, I daresay not one of the twenty leading physicists in this country would have even a casual interest in this subject. Likewise, interest in the philosophy of physics has dropped almost to zero among the bright young men; yet this field may simply be waiting for a new Ernst Mach who will stir it up and pave the way for another revolution like relativity. And we have all noticed such blind spots in the more technical fields, where it has suddenly been discovered, for example, how badly everyone has been neglecting oceanography, an area perhaps of central importance for our future food and resources.

I think these gaps cry out for reviewers and critics broadly trained and broadly read, who are competent to see what the neglected areas are and to encourage the young to go into them. A balanced and vigorous science requires a balanced and vigorous criticism. To paraphrase Clemenceau's remark that war is too important to be entrusted to generals, science is too important to be left to the scientists. Intelligent outside evaluation is good for a department, it is good for a university, and it would be good for science itself. The incompleteness of science is a challenge to great criticism. It is a challenge which I think will be met in the very finest presentations of science to the public.

THE LIFE OF MAN

It is a thrilling thing to be participating as actor or observer in the scientific revolution of our times, as science enters and transforms the life of man. Some are depressed by the hard work that must be done to make a world, and by the constant threat of failure and catastrophe. Some say philosophy has failed. I think this is only a momentary lapse between the old philosophy and the new that rises already in the laboratories. I think this century marks in history a revolution in man's outlook even more profound, if possible, than the accompanying revolution in science and technology. Man has suddenly found himself. He has explored all the earth and stepped outside it. He taps the sun's source of energy and stands ready to manipulate the weather and use the oceans. He measures back to the beginnings of time and out to the ends of space and sees his own sudden emergence, a thinking creature spun out of light and air and water and holding power in his hand, yet probably only one of millions of such creatures on other worlds.

And the power man holds is not only technical power but something far greater still, evolutionary power. He creates new species of plants and animals, halts or speeds up evolution, manipulates heredity like chemistry, and prepares to turn his own flimsy organism into whatever fantastic and brilliant and powerful form he most desires. The whole future is open-ended, waiting for us. This is not a time of philosophical decay but a time of birth. In the midst of our worry and fear, man reasoning, man the creator, is about to be born. The old philosophies will burst off and blow away, unable to contain so fierce a fire. From now on, in every century, man will look back and say: This was the one.

When we speak of the sweep and excitement of science, we are speaking of the cradle of man.

2. STYLE IN SCIENCE

IT HARDLY needs to be said that all scientists are not alike.
Look at any laboratory or university science department.
Professor Able is the kind of man who seizes an idea as a
dog seizes a stick, all at once. As he talks you can see him
stop short, with the chalk in his fingers, and then almost
jump with excitement as the insight grips him. His colleague, Baker, on the other hand, is a man who comes to
understand an idea as a worm might understand the same
stick, digesting it a little at a time, drawing his conclusions
cautiously, and tunneling slowly through it from end to end
and back again.

Which of these methods is likely to make the greater
contribution to science? There are drawbacks to both.
Able is volatile. He may drop his idea as rapidly as he acquired it. In a short time he can race through a forest of
ideas and leave all his colleagues breathless behind, including Baker. Baker is scornful of such a procedure, perhaps a
little envious. He can never try so many ideas, though in
the end each one he tries becomes part of him, each one
tested in every aspect.

Or consider another pair of scientific minds, whose contrasted inner workings are revealed by their contrasted foot-
note habits.

Charlson is the one who discovers everything for himself.
He dislikes reading other men's efforts because they stale

the fresh springs of his thought. Though he is famous to the world, his scientific enemies are numbered by the dozens because he never bothered to look up their prior parallelisms and dim anticipations. So he left out all the references that would have been their tendril grasps on fame. Rumors of plagiarism are heard at the Society meetings.

Doctor Doggett, instead, is footnote-happy. No historical cranny is safe. He pries out the foreshadowings, the counterarguments, and the misprints. If he makes a creative contribution himself it is lost among the references, for there are more lines of footnotes than there are of text. Yet he gathers a thousand strands together and may find distant connections which pass unnoticed by other men.

Will it be Doggett or Charlson who makes the great discovery?

This is a question we could pursue through the whole academic alphabet, contrasting the syndromes and merits of the types of scientific personality. Simply as writers, one man is dull, one witty; one verbose, another terse. This man's equations lie like boulders on the page, that man's like a fog. It is amusing to see how the differences show through the attempted impersonality of scientific verbiage.

But we would soon realize that the question of relative merit hinges on a more fundamental question: Is personality significant for science? We often hear the arguments for scientific determinism, which is the belief that scientific discoveries are somewhat like the measles, breaking out everywhere at once when the time is ripe. If this is so, is not one man in a given field as likely as another to make an important discovery? Does it make any difference to knowledge who invents a thing first, or what kind of mind and style he has?

If we look at some examples from the history of science

with this problem in mind, I think we will see that personality does indeed make a difference. The two aspects interpenetrate. To a remarkable extent the discovery ripe to be born selects one discoverer from among the contestants, picking out the master of a line of thought and method essential to its birth. But equally remarkable is the extent to which the undetermined and peculiar stamp of his parenthood is embedded forever in the body of pure knowledge.

DETERMINISM IN DISCOVERY

The evidence for scientific determinism — with its lesser emphasis on personality — is the familiar catalogue of the instances of multiple discovery. The great cases of this kind were the simultaneous and independent discovery of the calculus by Newton and Leibnitz three centuries ago, and the simultaneous Darwin and Wallace discoveries of natural selection in the last century. Hundreds of lesser examples could be listed. Each idea, with variations, is found and found again. Patent lawyers make their living from such competition.

Independent discoveries are sometimes only months or weeks apart, especially today in the fields crowded with first-rate competitors. In physics, for example, the synchrocyclotron was invented simultaneously in the United States and in Russia. Independent communications from this country and from Germany announced the current theoretical "shell model" of atomic nuclei in the very same issue of the *Physical Review*. The race for priority hinges on days, and the Saturday afternoon Letter-to-the-Editor becomes a regular event.

Such examples make scientific developments appear almost inevitable, maturing like dandelions on both sides of company fences and national ones, to the despair of Congressmen and drug houses. The reason for this is that discoveries have preconditions that must be met. Once these are met, even a non-genius may make a discovery if he is playing with the right apparatus and tries everything. To a certain extent, science is successful because it is a code of rules that enable ordinary brains with ordinary motivations to set up, one step at a time, the necessary preconditions.

Some are mechanical. Take the discoveries of electrons and of X-rays, which occurred within two years of each other in the 1890's. Both required the application of a high voltage to a good vacuum. This in turn required the knowledge of direct current electricity, a good cheap high-voltage generator, and a good cheap vacuum pump, with an electric motor drive for convenience. All these are late-nineteenth-century items. The incandescent lamp, not a discovery but an invention, had similar preconditions; but it could be made with a lower voltage and a poorer vacuum, and so was invented a few years earlier.

This is not to say that these discoveries could have been predicted. No one foresaw that such phenomena existed. But if anything were there to be found with that apparatus, it must have been found *then*. The discoveries were made by highly competent experimenters; yet within a few years almost any intelligent student might have made them independently, while experimenters ten times as competent could scarcely have set the dates of discovery earlier by as much as two decades. In present times, the anti-proton could be predicted, and planned for at Berkeley, years in advance; and then discovered almost as soon as the apparatus was designed, finished, and turned on. We can see why one celebrated physicist said that half of his success consisted in knowing what to order and where to order it.

There are also intellectual conditions that must be met, before a discovery can be made or appreciated or understood. The brilliant idea requires intellectual groundwork and, what is equally important, a scientific community ready for the novelty. It is just as sure a recipe for failure to have the right idea fifty years too soon as five years too late. William James might have been advising young men in any science when he said: Decide what important thing will be done in the next twenty years; then do it.

Occasionally, untimely ideas do get preserved to be marveled at. In mathematics, Fermat's Last Theorem still tantalizes us; and Hamilton's Quaternions, which were thought by his contemporaries to indicate mild insanity, were simply premature by two or three generations.

Abbé Mendel, father of genetics, actually bred his sweet peas decades too soon. His contribution was finally disinterred at the time when it could be understood. Roentgen made the discovery of X-rays in a momentary lapse from a lifelong study of crystals, which was no doubt equally painstaking and inspired but is almost unremembered because it was fifty years too early. Sometimes even a short time makes a great difference in the response to a new idea. Stories persist that the equations of quantum mechanics were derived by this man or that but were rejected by editors only a year or two before Schrödinger got his version accepted and won a Nobel prize.

We may speculate on how many good scientists may have died mute, inglorious, and bitter because their work was too advanced to be understood. This is the standard defense of the ill-prepared and the crackpot. Yet the failure to recognize a brilliant man is only partly due to the stupidity or stubbornness of the scientific community; it is also partly his own fault.

For brilliance has an obligation not only to create but also to communicate. A scientist cannot really go "voyaging through strange seas of thought alone." The more penetrating eye will see him to be surrounded by a cloud of witnesses. He takes from others; he gives to others. He must address the problems of his time. He must translate his thoughts into the language of his contemporaries. He must scatter them abroad for interaction. A thought which has not penetrated to other minds will die unfruitful.

As a result, the scientist can hardly be recognized posthumously, like the artist or poet. He is much less independent, much more bound to the current needs and purposes of the scientific community. His achievement of thought needs to be at the same time an achievement of communication and leadership which must be acknowledged by the group — by at least *one* editor! — before its intellectual viability fades away.

It is a perishable achievement. Not many of us know who first cut the trees or cleared the land beside our houses. The scientific explorer, like the wilderness explorer, exists to be superseded. Wandering at random, he finds a first, clumsy way to the new goal. The more important the goal, the greater the speed with which his path is by-passed by short cuts, ridden over by electronic computing machines, and obliterated by the marching masses of Ph.D.'s. His hesitations, his sextant readings, the art and intuition by which he avoided this pitfall or that rabbit track — these make dull hard reading after a few years, for they apply to a world of difficulties which, because of his very efforts, has vanished and can scarcely be reconstructed. But such a man is properly contemptuous of the incoherent genius whose ravishing discoveries are too strange and vague to be communicable.

KINDS OF MINDS

Determinism also plays a more intimate role. Not only is the time of a discovery approximately determined, it seems that the personality of the discoverer may to some extent be determined. To find America, we must have a fifteenth-century Western sea captain, uncommercial, convinced, dogged, persuasive, with delusions of grandeur — whether his name is Columbus or something else.

To see this principle in science, we must concentrate on two components of personality which I shall call method and style. By method, I mean the type of a scientist's intuition, his normally preferred method of attack. One man loves most to design and build apparatus, a glorified instrument maker. Another is a human measuring engine who can turn out more data or more precise data than anyone else. Some like to improve on other men's experiments in familiar fields, others prefer wild and novel experiments of their own at the limit of the possible. In these differences, one major axis of variation ought to be especially emphasized. It is the difference between the generally inductive and the generally deductive types of mind.

In an inductive mind, the internal monologue might go somewhat as follows: "Now here's a funny result. It doesn't fit in at all with Smollengoble's theorem! Yes, the apparatus is okay. Didn't I see last month where someone else had trouble with that theorem? But he had lower pressure. If we increased the pressure, would it go farther in the same direction?"

The general from the particular. This is the man who covers his laboratory walls with graphs of his data and squints at them every morning before he turns on his power supply, wondering if those deviations are experimental error or a real effect. There is something of this turn of mind in all of us. A talented few, like the master organic chemists, develop it until they can play their residues and hunches as a virtuoso plays the violin.

The deductive genius may be tone-deaf to such music. His passion is not for the uncertain new order but for elegance and clarity in the old. At his highest pinnacle, he is the Euclid or Maxwell who stands and looks back after a period of growth and sees that a few simple postulates will unite a whole body of separate rules into a symmetrical system.

Like the inductive mind, he sees patterns, but in a different medium. Perhaps when he closes his eyes by the fire he stares into a magnificent void where the luminous theorems move and intersect and enclose each other and he leaps up shouting, "I have it! I have it!" However jumbled his desk may be, there is some distant region of the spirit where his files are clearly labeled and his papers have been written in a neat hand on one side only and are stapled into bundles with their edges straight — the great plan encompassing every particular in every pigeonhole. There is something of this, too, in all of us.

One of these minds anticipates, the other reconstructs. Inductive steps must come before deductive ones. So in each subject area there is a time when one method is most appropriate. Then it exhausts its material, at least for the moment, and recedes as the important discoveries begin to fall to another kind of mental machine. A field of knowledge has a curve of growth and a morphology, branches and stem — a beginning, a middle, and an end. Different talents are needed in the gardeners at different times. Those with a green thumb must plant, while others with a sure balance climb ladders later for the fruit.

Take the discovery of the law of gravitation. First there is visual observation and instrumentation, from the ancients to Tycho Brahe's quadrant and his tables of years of nights of measurement. Then there are the rule-makers, from the Ptolemaic astronomers to Kepler, who asked how all this would look from the nearest star and searched Tycho's tables for regularities, boiling the regularities down to his three laws of planetary motion.

Wandering in and out of the procession are the speculators — Lucretius, Copernicus — who animate the mixture with their lively controversies. At one side are the auxiliaries: Archimedes on conic sections; the navigators, defining the shape and size of the earth; Galileo, hurling balls and abstracting from them that ingenious invention, the ideal free body.

What a preparation for Newton! It might be compared to some biblical prophecy in its visions and connections and anticipations across the millenniums. These are the shoulders of giants, with linked arms — not merely a human pyramid, but the braced and giant framework of knowledge itself.

The main line of development in scientific theory follows this sequence of work methods: observation, rule of thumb, speculation, synthesis. Naturally the methods of work are not perfectly separated in time nor even in the individual scientists. Every research man must be capable of performing all the functions in some degree — especially the speculative function — if he is to be worth his scientific salt. He may even have several highly developed talents, like Newton. This should not blind us to the big difference in the different mental processes, even such as that between the maker of the important little first syntheses — frequently an experimenter — and the maker of final grand syntheses who often shows a native distaste for the raw and original datum.

To see the historical necessity that selects these types, let us try a thought experiment on history. Consider what would have happened if the minds of Newton and Kepler had been interchanged. The slightest acquaintance with the work of either man will show that Newton's mind was not the one to unravel Tycho's data, and Kepler's was not the one to do Newton's necessary preliminary work of discovering the calculus. Not that it would have been absolutely impossible; only that it would have been slow and burdensome for either mind to try to use intuition methods like the other, and that they would have turned aside soon and wisely to more congenial discoveries.

A mature research worker needs to seek out tasks which he can undertake best with his mental gifts at his moment of history. A Maxwell in the eighteenth century could not have united electricity and magnetism but would have had to work on, let us say, astronomy, while the Franklins did the groundwork of electricity. Maxwell in the nineteenth century could and did perfect electricity but would have been lost in atomic spectra, where a Kepler kind of mind was needed. A Maxwell today might find chemistry or field-theory almost ripe for his talents, but would probably be foolish to go back to the well-plowed area of electricity unless he proposed to make a still larger synthesis, or a synthesis from a completely new point of view.

GIVE AND TAKE OF TALENTS

The time sequence of work methods is never perfectly clear-cut, however; in a single field the different types of talent coexist and make simultaneous contributions. For the different types of talent need each other. Inductive and deductive, intuitive and classical, are the two halves of a pair of scissors and cut only when they are opposed. Each work method produces its own peculiar excesses which must be seen from another viewpoint before their deformity can be recognized.

The inductive mind often goes too far. Not having the advantage of the grand synthesis, it does not know where to stop. Searching for important relations, it finds unimportant ones. Experimental error may be turned into law, or clear disproof dismissed as experimental error.

Pythagoras' useful relation between the sides of triangles seems to have been associated in his own enthusiasm with the lengths of musically harmonious strings, and so with the harmonies of the universe and the music of the spheres. This goes too far, but it is not all nonsense: the lengths of harmonious strings do indeed have simple numerical ratios.

The first regularity of planets which Kepler thought he found was that they moved on spheres circumscribed and inscribed in five vast regular polyhedrons in the heavens.

This is not all nonsense: the regular spacing of the orbits is a main feature of several recent cosmologies.

Such jumps "beyond reason" need to be continuously criticized by the deductive and classical mind. Yet the inductive mind is like a sentry who must be forgiven for firing at an occasional shadow provided he always fires toward the enemy.

The sin of the deductive mind is that it derides and suppresses those inductive jumps that later prove to be right about as harshly as those that prove wrong. Newton rejected Huyghens' and Hooke's wave theory of light which swept out Newton's own ideas a hundred years later. An esteemed critic showed that Balmer's formula, the first real regularity found in atomic spectra, must be a mathematical accident. De Broglie's paper, which contained the first germ of quantum mechanics, was widely regarded as nonsense.

Still, this conservatism has a good result. The success of an innovator is meted out in proportion to his scientific persuasiveness, his patience in amassing crucial observations, like Darwin, to show that the old faith is unjustified. It is not the moment of insight but the moment of acceptance that marks a firm step forward. Scientific growth is by conflict. The truth is found only in the heat of controversy as each man is forced to defend his thesis: the classicist his sufficiency, the innovator his necessity.

The historical counterpoint between the inductive and deductive mind is useful even in its subtler manifestations. It provides an unspectacular tension which is a major force in keeping science balanced. Each creative worker lives in a steady stream of deductive criticism — normally, in fact, self-criticism — curbing and channeling his intuitive impulses. It is not so much that his little daily jumps and inferences must not violate "reason" as that they must satisfy more delicate canons of scientific good taste. How many readings or decimal places to take; what precautions; how ignorant or speculative to show oneself at various stages of scientific friendship; how soon to publish; and so on. A large part of the training of science students is really devoted to instilling this code of scientific manners.

The code is a balance of opposites. A man may acquire deductive good manners at the expense of some of his inductive hope, faith, and fire; fanning the fire may soften in turn the rigor of his self-criticism. Some individuals and groups try to solve the problem by separating the two processes, starting with an idea stage in which the imagination runs wild and free, followed by an analytical stage in which the ideas are critically selected and combined. The genius is the one who can maximize both elements and maintain at the same time the fiercest productivity and the most exacting standards.

Likewise for a successful scientific group, the curbing of inductive jumps by the canons of taste must be neither too rigid nor too loose. The scissors will not cut if the blades are locked or if they are wobbly. The rigor of editors is needed to restrict the wilder flights as much as the zeal of speculators is needed to keep knowledge alive. The delicacy and importance of this balance may account in part for the enormous variations in achievement from country to country and from time to time. Science cannot be fruitful where publishers indulge unready authors, wild fancies, and incompetent techniques; nor where hoary academic despots hold the seats of power and press the young men to a mold two generations old. But neither side can afford to be dogmatic, for it is only in the light of the syntheses of a succeeding generation that we can look back and be certain what was excess of speculation and what was excess of repression.

STYLE IN CREATIVITY

These remarks have perhaps conveyed some idea of the depth to which scientific determinism goes. A social necessity fixes not only the timing of a discovery but the work methods of the discoverer; it affects the heat of the controversies engendered, and where science is successful it sets the canons of taste which determine whether the discovery is accepted or rejected at a given stage of proof.

Nevertheless, all is not fixed. If we move about inside this framework we can now begin to see the ornaments and gargoyles added, unnecessarily and delightfully and sometimes unexpectedly, by exuberant craftsmen, shaped by personality above and beyond strict scientific need.

For one thing, each person has his own combination of fields of interest. A scientist trained in one subject often makes spectacular contributions when his novel outlook and work methods are turned into another field. Think of the special approach of Helmholtz, the physiologist turned physicist; or of Pasteur, the chemist, among the diseases.

Personality also enters through language, with its hidden assumptions. Without Newton himself, we might never have had "force" or "mass" in the equations of motion; or they might have had very different definitions and emphases. Philosophers have pulled and hauled at them for centuries; the difficulties were ineradicable, because these symbols were written from the beginning in the Newtonian equations that worked. The Father of Physics has imprinted "force" and "mass," like intellectual genes, into every cell of the physical sciences today.

Kepler, on the other hand, seems to have eschewed, largely on aesthetic grounds, the anthropomorphic concept of "force" between heavenly bodies. In this question of taste, he anticipates Einstein. If history had put the Kepler mind in the Newton body, it might have delayed the discovery of universal gravitation, which would have been difficult for Kepler — but it might have accelerated the discovery of general relativity.

Terminology is often chained to such initial biases. Franklin's choice of the arithmetic terms "positive" and "negative" to designate the two supplementary types of electricity still plagues our thinking and may have delayed who knows what happier synthesis.

The idiosyncrasies of taste and choice, of abilities and workmanship, embellish and modify a discovery. The work method is determined; the style is not. Any physical law is exhibited in many places and forms and may be found by single experiments on hundreds of compounds or by hundreds of experiments on a grain of sand. And the discoverer may be an exhibitionist, or a conservative; an equation maker, or a model maker; he may want priority, or certainty. He may succeed by testing everything to destruction, at unusual temperatures and pressures; or by exploring his materials with nothing but a beam of light. He may be guided by shrewd and almost superstitious hunches, that only fluorocarbons will give him clear-cut answers, or density-matrix methods, or Drosophila, or sweet peas.

Sometimes the effects of such variations are profound indeed. There is one instance where a vast intellectual development has been hung on the deficiencies of a single piece of apparatus. We might not believe that electrons are in atoms except for some equipment assembled in 1898 by Zeeman in Holland, with which he found that the spectrum lines of atoms were broadened and polarized by a magnetic field. This "Zeeman effect" was explained by Lorentz on the assumption that the atoms contained the newly discovered corpuscles called electrons. Later, Bohr continued to assume this in his atomic theory; and whole-electrons-in-atoms passed on into the quantum mechanics that we now use.

But meanwhile, what of the Zeeman effect? If Zeeman had had a better spectrograph or had improved his apparatus before publishing his first results, he would have reported what a college senior can discover now: that each of his broadened spectrum lines is really a complex array of many lines, with every array different. Neither Lorentz nor anyone else would then have believed that there were intact electrons, all alike, inside the atom; perhaps fractional ones would have been assumed. The Bohr atom would have been different, or impossible. Quantum mechanics as we know it might never have appeared. No doubt some other theoretical system would have been produced in its place, but by now, after fifty years, its practitioners would speak a language incomprehensible or perhaps unbelievable to our best physicists. (The scientists will not find it any easier to talk to scientists they meet from another planet than laymen will.)

If a piece of apparatus can shape a field of knowledge, a brilliant scientist may also have a great personal effect. Many of the peculiarities of modern physics seem to have this individual stamp. Bohr, de Broglie, Schrödinger, Heisenberg, Dirac — each is responsible for some aspect of the synthesis of atomic structure which is quantum mechanics. Yet their approaches are very different: Bohr with his electron-orbits in space; de Broglie with his almost mystical waves; Schrödinger with his differential equations; Heisenberg with his matrices and strict operationalism; Dirac with his formalism. If we had lost one of these, it would not have affected our ability to predict experimental results, which is often said to be the aim of science; but it would have been a great loss indeed to our understanding.

And a great change. Without Bohr himself, would the earlier ideas of an atom as a vibrating jelly have been strangely modified by some other young pseudo-Bohr in the 1910's to explain the spectra and win the day? Without the particular style of a particular man, Dirac, we might have had formalism of a sort, but probably not the chaste, terse, awful elegance that now strikes fear and admiration into the graduate students.

The work of Willard Gibbs in chemical thermodynamics may be the most individual tour de force of all. Somewhat cut off in late-nineteenth-century America from the larger body of European theoretical physicists and chemists, he evolved an unusual kind of thinking; perhaps as an island population evolves aberrant species when cut off from the mainland. His equations show no trace of the mechanical particles bombarding the walls of a box which still dominated the thought of European scientists. He produced a theory without "forces" and without imaginary models of what was happening in the box, using simply relations among the things observed on the outside, such as temperature, pressure, and volume. And he combined these with a logical absolute, a naked and apparently vulnerable assertion about entropy.

True, this was not completely alien to contemporary

style. Differential equations like his were the admired mathematical form in other areas. There had been some interest in the physical power of syllogisms; and Mach and Einstein were shortly to remove "force" from motion and from gravitation and to assert other logical absolutes. But taken together and applied to chemistry, what a change! Small wonder that nobody noticed him but Maxwell. Small wonder that the best science students still go blank and dumb, and the little philosophy major at the back of the room suddenly begins to get the right answers, when they come to this part of the course. It hurts a three-dimensional man to see temperature computed from a syllogism.

It seems probable to me that if Gibbs had lived in England or Germany this fusion of ideas might not have occurred until at least a generation later. By that time chemical thinking would have been set in another mold, and chemistry today would be a different thing.

There are many lessons, for our culture, for our teachers, and for our scientists, to be learned from examining closely the interplay of the Great Man aspect of history with the Determinist aspect. It is exhibited in the microcosm of the scientific world in a relatively simple form in which the causal intellectual strands are rather easy to trace. The general cultural or political historian might find this limited but precisely known area a good testing ground for theories of history.

I think he would conclude, as I have here, that the nature of the achievements of a large competing scientific group is determined by the group and its history, and depends little on the behavior of individual discoverers. We can almost write down equations for the speed and scope of advance in some departments of knowledge. But the pressure of scientific determinism becomes weak and random as we approach the great unitary syntheses. For they are not only discoveries. They are also artistic creations, shaped by the taste and style of a single hand.

3. COMPETITION
IN CREATION

EVERY field of biology needs a test animal — some bug or beast easy to grow and handle and analyze. Genetics has its fruit flies, physiology its hamsters, and animal psychology its rats. I am beginning to think that the best test animals for human social psychology would be the creative organisms that we call art and science. In their creative aspects these fields are somewhat isolated from the rest of the world and form a microcosm where we could trace the fundamental interactions between minds more simply and directly than in the buzzing, blooming confusion of society outside.

Some day, no doubt, a mathematical theory will be perfected to describe such interactions and their causal sequences and time constants. Even now a few social historians and psychologists are probably working on such problems. But the age of individual insights is not yet past, and I think it is worth setting down what seem to me to be the important social factors in the creative process. In the long run, every interpretation we can get from the participants, both artists and scientists, will help us further toward understanding this peculiar form of human behavior.

CREATIVE ACTIVITY

As I see it, the directions taken by creative activity can be understood in terms of two basic concepts, the concept of creation-space and the concept of a repulsion between creators. Creation-space I envisage as a mathematically more precise and general form of the common notion of a "field" or "area of activity," that is, a region in which individual creative contributions can be located. Visualize it as an ordinary three-dimensional volume if you like, but it might have many dimensions, like the "hyperspaces" familiar to physicists and mathematicians. The boundaries of the volume are the fundamental limitations set by the nature of the field. For example, in the field of paintings there are obvious physical limitations, such as that a picture and all its details must lie within a humanly manageable range of sizes, the colors must lie within our spectrum, with their distinctions matched to our discrimination, and so on. But the picture can be described in more subtle dimensions also, that of style, for example, in which it may lie somewhere between realism and abstraction, or between the photographic and the Impressionist; or the dimensions of organization, of tradition, and many others.

The second concept, of repulsion between creators, may be less familiar. It is the notion that no two individuals will occupy the same point in this creation-space, and indeed that when we have many creative artists in a field they will tend to move as far apart as possible so as to fill every corner of the field accessible to them.

There is an old physical doctrine that two bodies cannot be in the same place at the same time. This is a primitive fact (or perhaps a condition of perception) which we like to verbalize in today's language by speaking of the Pauli principle and of repulsion between closed shells of electrons. It is an equally primitive biological fact that two organisms cannot be in the same place at the same time. Every organism resists attack or incorporation in another. This is part of what we mean by integrity. An organism that accepts incorporation, and the resultant hindered or conflicting decision systems, accepts a lower chance of survival; Napoleon said he always preferred to fight against allies. I suspect that our psychological urge for individual assertion, like most psychology, is a specialized form of a deeper biological necessity. It seems to me that the primitive fact of social psychology, in creation-space or in opinion-space or in any of several other hyperspaces we might name, is that no two men can hold the same positions at the same time. However united they may appear to the outside world, they will not be able to sit down together for two minutes without beginning to examine their differences.

I know that these "spaces" and "points" smack of the geometry book. Many readers may be resentful or contemptuous of the poor physicist who wants to pin human activity down to a set of coordinates. Very well. I have tried to be mathematically explicit so as to be clear, but I will now agree immediately that there would be a real problem in ever measuring such spaces or points or even in determining how many dimensions there are — although similar problems are solved daily in market research and factor analysis — and there is plenty of room for you to turn around again and make them as vague or uncertain or humane as you please. But it seems to me that these ideas are but a formal restatement of the descriptions used by many creative artists and scientists themselves. There are readers who may feel, quite oppositely, that it is all the typical professor's trick of restating in pedantic language what everybody knows. Here I plead guilty: this is indeed my intention, because I think the pedantic language gives us a new point and range of view and permits a precise description which may someday help us to predict some of the tides of creative activity in a useful and accurate way.

REPULSION AND COHESION

To see how these principles work, let us look a little more closely at the repulsion between men and how it shows itself.

When people are brought together in a dormitory or a discussion club, they spend many of their first hours establishing their differences. In an army barracks, one boy gets to be called the quiet one and is teased for it and identified with it, although he might have been the noisiest in the quiet home from which he came. He may retreat into himself and the others become still noisier, to establish their difference. Another man gets the reputation of the great lover and tries to live up to it, another the great backslapper, and so on. In a short time all the dimensions of personality that are needed for identification become explored and magnified. Looking out from the center of the group, we see them projected on the social sky, Henry northwest in politics and forty degrees up toward vanity, Joe at the pole of leadership for us, Charles at the nadir of stupidity. We have become oriented, we move in familiar surroundings; just as in the suburb we are pleased when we first locate the school and the grocery store with respect to our new house, and are able to find our way home from either.

Some persons may be acutely aware of their local surroundings in psycho-social space. A child's feeling for the micromilieu of his family and friends is probably about as important to his security — and about as instinctive — as his feeling for the microgeographical surroundings, what chair he is sitting on, how far away he is from the fire, and which direction is up. He maneuvers his hopes and plans around the repeated experience of finding brother more gullible, mother more scatterbrained, father more mule-headed. In such a family, such a child soon becomes the champion of guile, logic, and liberalism.

Moving from group to group, a man may find his opinions projected on another sky and so may turn them around from time to time, keeping them flexible. But the members of the little hill-communities, the old peoples' home, the sisters in the big mansion growing up and growing old together, they have their polarities fixed in opinion-space and behavior-space from an early age, and they form a crystallized constellation, rigid and brittle. They resent the intrusion of forces that might produce motion in their little world: they shoot at strangers and burn witches.

HANGING TOGETHER

In any group, of course, we do not fly completely apart in defining our differences. Peripheral members of the debating club may drop out from an excess of ridicule or neglect, but the members who are left have some cohesion. They hang together, like the unprotected and gregarious herbivores we are descended from. The family, for all its differences, is pressed together by its greater differences from the society outside; once we go out, we recoil, realizing how many premises we had in common and that Father is just like me, after all. Our behavior in psychosocial space does not resemble the molecules of a gas flying as far apart as possible — if it did, we should have no large cities — but rather the molecules of a liquid, careful not to fuse or lose our identity, preserving our separateness, but keeping in contact in droplets and hamlets and nations, and moving our positions only under local pressure as new molecules crowd in. The Quaker in the old story says it well, "I think the whole world is queer except me and thee; and sometimes I think thee is a little queer."

The physical analogy may suggest to the psychologist several important parameters to measure in this space. But there is also an obvious analogy with the well-known doctrine that every ecological niche in a biological system will be filled. If an important central member leaves a group, it is easy to see and feel the changes of attitude of the other members as they shift their positions to take advantage of the new space that is left to them; or, from a molecular point of view, as they crowd into the vacant site. This can be seen most clearly in spontaneous social groups that have little or no formal and official structure. Similarly, a group tends to force a newcomer into the place of a departed member if it is at all possible, and almost everyone who has been a newcomer to an old group has had the experience of having to make a violent resistance against being erroneously identified with some ghostly point of view.

We pay special attention to the boundaries between our positions in attitude-space. The nodal surfaces within the family are defined by a hundred quarrels. The political chalkmark is there on the floor and we stand up to it toe to toe, ready to slug it out if it takes all a lifetime. Whosoever is not for me is against me. The sharpness of these boundaries no doubt has its origin in the biological necessity of making a clean, all-or-none decision. This must also be why the boundaries are so much a matter of emotion and so little of logic.

We could go on to discuss what stabilizes our boundaries,

for example in moral judgments, where the Puritan conscience divides the world into good and evil; or in politics, where in one country a majority electoral law stabilizes a boundary down the middle and preserves a two-party system while in another a proportional-representation law stabilizes factional boundaries and "atomizes the electorate." But the interesting question here is the application of these notions to the style-spaces of the various creative arts. And some readers will by now have realized that I have been talking all along not about discussion clubs and families but about the creative behavior of artists and scientists. The barracks was the school of artists or the research institute, and the hill community was the Chemical Society or the great Academy.

THE CROWDING OF HISTORY

In fact in art, as in science, we have not only contemporaneous stylistic repulsions between artists but also, to the extent that works of art are preserved, we have historical repulsions reaching out of the past over long periods of time to act on present artists. There is relatively little pressure of the distant past on family feuds. It has more effect on the boundaries of political debate. But in the arts, the past is with us for as long as the record. We have not forgotten that Homer called it "the wine-dark sea," and until the memory of Homer is completely obliterated, no self-respecting writer will be able to use this combination of words again except in a context of Homeric allusion. In sculpture, an almost-Venus-de-Milo, no matter how brilliantly executed, means something less dramatic and less creative just because there has already been one.

The result is that the artist has to define and defend his

differences from all his predecessors as carefully as from his contemporaries. Hemingway said he was competing only with the dead. But unfortunately the predecessors are almost immovable. If we could watch the style-space of any one of the creative arts or sciences as it is filled up in the course of history, we should see the great masters sweeping into a young field, and, like great boulders, filling volumes of space around some central position. Successors must squeeze themselves into the available regions between, like smaller stones. Their pebble followers are confined to still smaller spaces, and so on until the spaces become too small for creation or self-respect and the field is exhausted. It must wait for new materials or language, new social relations or a new audience, to enlarge the original creation-space so that there comes to be room for a new creative act of organization.

I am not denying the importance of schools of art and science — there is cohesion here, just as in families — and it would be interesting to explore the subtle details of educational method or environment that permit a strong school to grow and prosper around one teacher at one place and time and not around another. But my concern here is not with the continuity which is necessary for education and understanding but with the divergence which is necessary for creation. The central problem for the great masters — for the artists, as distinguished from the craftsmen — is the competition with history.

André Malraux says,

No man can build on the void, and a civilization that breaks with the style at its disposal soon finds itself empty-handed . . . [But he goes on to say] whether partial or thorough-going, the will to outdo the past operates in the same manner whenever the artist is confronted with a given form and feels impelled to refashion it in another form . . . Just as the rift between the artist and the period preceding his compels him to modify its form, and that between him and his masters to alter theirs, so the difference between his present self and the man he was, compels him to change his own forms, too, in the course of his career.

In such terms, even those of us who are not experts can understand, for example, the spectacular rise and the equally spectacular disappearance of photographic realism in painting and sculpture and of naturalism in the theater. There was a goal to be reached; it was reached; it was then time to do something else. The principle is not confined to the plastic arts.

T. S. Eliot says,

Milton made a great epic impossible for succeeding generations; Shakespeare made a great poetic drama impossible; such a situation is inevitable, and it persists until the language has so altered that there is no danger, because no possibility, of imitation. Anyone who tries to write poetic drama, even today, should know that half of his energy must be exhausted in the effort to escape from the constricting toils of Shakespeare: the moment his attention is relaxed, or his mind fatigued, he will lapse into bad Shakespearian verse. For a long time after an epic poet like Milton, or a dramatic poet like Shakespeare, nothing can be done.

The pressure of past excellence on the artist, forcing him to do something outside these filled creation sites, can lead him to wild explorations and distortions. Recently some poetry and painting has seemed to be scraping the bottom to find some untouched obscurity worthy of exploration. But this century, with its magnificent realization that art, like music and geometry, can have a formal structural beauty independent of any external reference, has given to both fields a previously neglected creation-space — *"another* world," Malraux calls it — which they have only begun to explore. And architecture, presented with a great empty creation-space of novel materials, seems indeed to be entering a new classical era.

THE CREATIVE FUTURE

In science also, the past closes doors for us. The late-comers must nibble on auxiliary theorems and minor consequences. After Schrödinger's paper appears, no physicist wants to solve the hydrogen atom by that method again, except as a pastiche. He must go on to new atoms or molecules or new methods. But the novelty is not cyclical as it sometimes seems to be in art. It has often been said that science progresses, but art does not progress. It is true that a Lachaise nude is not a Praxiteles, but who can say for certain that one is "better" or "more advanced" than the other?

In our terms, what such questions are getting at is that, by comparison with the art-spaces, the creative world of science is very large, and probably infinite. The artist need shed no tears. Working in a limited space means that a great artist's problem and his solution will still be an important problem and an interesting solution after thousands of years. This is never the case in science. There, any problems but the very deepest are quickly outmoded. Generation after generation, the scientific studies proliferate in every realm and move out to open up and exhaust new realms. At the end of the eighteenth century, a great French physicist lamented, like a geopolitician or a decadent poet, that, since Newton, there were no more physical worlds to conquer. Michelson and others said this again at the end of the nineteenth century. They were premature. From sand grain we have proceeded to microbe, from microbe to molecule, to atoms, to nuclei, a whole kingdom at every level. And in the other direction, our imaginations have expanded from solar systems to galaxies to universes of galaxies.

Looking into the almost-infinite past, we contemplate not merely the Deluge, but successive orders of antiquity, the glaciers, the dinosaurs, the creation of planets, and the creation of elements. We search the ocean depths and outer space, write equations for the weather and for the evolution of species, probe the connections within our brains and the relations of nations. This ocean of truth will never be exhausted. From the physicist's point of view, there will always be further relations among the 10^{80} atoms in the universe that we have not comprehended with the mere 10^{20} brain cells of the human race. From the psychologist's point of view, everything that we know about the universe is contained in some small part of those cells, so that even when our knowledge of the external world is complete enough to satisfy us, there will still be relations among these cells left for still further cells to know.

I think this means that there is more hope than ever for the creative future. To quote Malraux once more, "Every artist of genius . . . becomes a transformer of the meaning of the world, which he masters by reducing it to forms he has selected or invented, just as the philosopher reduces it to concepts and the physicist to laws." I see a time coming when even these historically separate disciplines will cease to be separate, when the various transformations of the meaning of the world will come to form a continuous spectrum, and it will not be possible to say of a great creator, "He is an artist," or "He is a physicist," any more than it was possible of Leonardo. In that day I think the artistic intelligence may finally discover that there is more room for its fulfillment, not in organizing the old language-space into further poetry or movement-space into further ballet, but in organizing knowledge-space into beautiful physical law, taking its aesthetic delight in the form and movement and implications and elegance of new ways of stating the equations of the world.

4. HOW FAR CAN
WE FORESEE?

IN EVERY generation for one or two centuries now, men have been marveling at how fast the world moves. A hundred years ago we find Thoreau writing of the rapid changes brought by the railroad and of the telegraph that will communicate from Maine to Texas. He adds, of course, that "Maine and Texas, it may be, have nothing important to communicate." In *Life on the Mississippi,* Mark Twain comments repeatedly with some little pride on the rapid technical and social changes taking place at the time. During the last fifty years, things have been happening so fast that one school of social scientists identifies "social lag" as one of the major problems of our society. No longer does it have much meaning to build houses or offices, or plan parks, to last for a century. The attempt begins to be fruitless. Anything we construct is likely to be obliterated well before a hundred years by some major rearrangement of our cities or highways, or it is likely to be made obsolete by new ways of living. Already many of the first steel skyscrapers of the early 1900's have been torn down to make room for much larger ones, or for parking lots.

These days a man can scarcely plan ahead even as far as his own retirement. Once he looked forward to the rocking chair surrounded by grandchildren. Now he anticipates a house trailer. What next? Those beaches you may have planned to park beside may be drowned or oil-slicked or radioactive before you reach them. In thirty years, the forests of the Arctic or the craters of the moon may be dictated by pressure and fashion and transportation as the ideal retiring places.

How can we bring up children in such a world? What moorings of the mind will hold them stable in this flux?

There are two ways, I think, to meet the problem of change. One is to learn to accept it, even to build our lives around it. Americans are getting to be old hands at this. As fast as the new arrives, a dozen media rush in to announce, to exhort, to debate, to smooth the path for mass acceptance of it — to sell. After only fifteen years of television we have rearranged our living rooms and our Saturday nights and our educational schemes and have come to a kind of stable truce with the little white screen. After fifteen years of atom bombs and rockets, even the loftiest of fools are beginning to act as if war had to be avoided. Whether their responses will indeed be fast enough or intelligent enough to escape disaster is another matter.

The other way to meet change is to anticipate it. Here I think we could do much better than we are now doing. We need to know how to plan ships and houses and insurance schemes for contingencies fifty to eighty years away. It takes twenty years to raise a child. It would help a lot to know what kind of world we are raising him for, not merely in its toys and excitements, but in the habits and customary comforts that will support his sanity. What broadened human interactions and responsibilities will he have to bear? How can he keep the new technological advances in their place as his servants and not his masters?

Up to the present, the general forecasts that might enable

us to answer such questions have not been very good. In limited areas, of course, such as the aircraft industry, missile development, atomic energy, or the census, forecasts and plans are made regularly for ten to twenty years ahead. Industrial laboratories commonly work on products that may take fifteen years to reach the market.

But the forecasts I am thinking of would be far more extensive than any of these. We need serious prophecies with a wider sweep, to cover the full range and interaction of human activities, and to run into the future for at least a lifetime. I know that there is much realistic science fiction that attempts such estimates, but it is hard to disentangle the real forecasts from the Jeremiads and space operas, or to separate the well-balanced estimate of the future from the private and salable hobbyhorse. I think it is time for universities and industries and government groups to turn long-range prophecy into a serious and responsible public business.

It is true that the future is uncertain. An auto trip is uncertain but this does not prevent us from making plans and appointments that we usually meet. And the future of society is not so obscure or uncertain as some may think.

To prove this, it is only necessary to look for a moment at some of the old scientific prophecies of a generation ago to see how accurately they have turned out — and just where they went wrong. Many of them, of course, are limited and erratic, just because one author, no matter how brilliant, can scarcely comprehend the full variety of the technical and social forces that are coming to birth at a given instant. We will see also that they tend to err in the same directions over and over again. But in many ways these forecasts are remarkably good, and it looks very much as if, by noting these systematic errors and correcting them, a well-informed group today could make prophecies more accurate than any that the human race has ever had.

"LOOKING BACKWARD" (1887)

Take Edward Bellamy's book of seventy years ago, *Looking Backward, 2000–1887*. This was a Socialist tract cast in the form of a Utopian novel, which had a great influence on the social thought of the last generation. It is hung on a dream formula and baited with a quaint love affair ("sugar crystal," Heywood Broun called it), but it seems to be meant as a serious description of the social and technological changes that could occur in a city such as Boston by the year 2000 if all men would work together toward Bellamy's socialist ideals.

What does it prophesy? Sociologically, that Boston could be a communal society, with money entirely replaced by ration cards. This does not look quite like Utopia to me, but from time to time, depending on what state of emergency we are in, it does look like a dull possibility for the future of society. On the technical side, however, Bellamy's most daring prediction is a kind of home radio or loudspeaker connected with a central station by telephone lines, with a choice of four programs. His heroine "merely touched one or two screws, and at once the room was filled with the music of a grand organ anthem." In Boston of that day, messages are to be shot from place to place by pneumatic tube, and all lighting will have become artificial.

All this was up to date when Bellamy wrote. The telephone, the pneumatic tube, the electric light, all belonged

to the previous twenty years or so. For us today the most
Utopian aspect of his marvels would be the quality of the
radio programs he imagined.

The dialogues in *Looking Backward* take place in the
home of a doctor, and much is made of his relation to his
patients and to the state. However the Bostonians of the
year 2000, although magnificent physical specimens (the
women have a "faultless luxuriance of figure"), will not
have been made so by the marvels of medicine. In 1887,
pasteurization and antisepsis were still being argued. X-rays
were eight years in the future. Medicine was still in the
hands of doctors and had no marvels. The physical superiority of people in the twenty-first century is to have been
achieved mostly by "the effect of untrammeled sexual selection." Up to date again. Darwin's theory of sexual selection
had been published in 1871. Mendel was unknown.

Bellamy's ideals in other matters also have a refined
Victorian quality. The stores of the year 2000 are to be like
Roman temples, the clothes are to be flowing robes, the
attitudes between the sexes are to be genteel. A few rare
spirits might wish the same today. It is all charming and in
many ways forgivable. One reform at a time. Socialism is
quite enough without reforming romance. A tract must
reach its own generation; and Bellamy's did. It was a best
seller and was translated into many languages.

But a Utopian who limits himself to the technology and
romance of his time, to the almost-believable, however good
his reasons, limits himself as a prophet. The most revolutionary party of Utopian reformers, complete with under-
cover agents and mass meetings, may not remake society
as fast as a single new invention. It is true that the prediction of gadgets and inventions has not usually been the

central purpose of Utopian tracts. Perhaps it should have been. A technological blemish may be the entering point for profound economic and social and political misconceptions. If a man does not know what is technically possible and probable, what new devices may stabilize or unstabilize the commerce between men, he is severely handicapped in knowing what is possible in politics or in the distribution of wealth. The desire for automobiles may bring economic and political equality faster than the desire for equality. In America, the year 1940 outdid Bellamy's 2000, perhaps in social reform as well as in automobiles.

"ANTICIPATIONS" (1902)

But if we turn to prophets who were better informed technically, we find similar errors. Take H. G. Wells's book, *Anticipations*, written in 1902. Wells, as we all know, was a marvelously successful forecaster. Decades before they appeared, he imagined nuclear weapons and robot battles, and space missiles reaching for the moon and Mars. The world today is ablaze with the glare of the Wellsian fantasies.

And *Anticipations* is not fiction but a serious attempt to estimate what can happen in the remaining ninety-eight years of the twentieth century. What does it predict? First, and most successfully, the social effects of the horseless carriage. Wells sees it multiplying into millions of private cars. He sees trucks and buses. Repair shops. Great roadways. Displacement of the railroad. Enlarged cities, with suburbs and commuters. And for war, "ironclad road fighting-machines."

An accurate picture and full of accurate social detail.

Wells is one of the best at anticipating the broad social consequences of invention. We can only wish he had gone further, to predict the effects of the automobile on daily life, on clothes and play and courtship.

But his transportation predictions for the whole century were fulfilled in twenty-five years! Airplanes? He ventures to say, "Very probably before 1950, a successful aeroplane will have soared and come home safe and sound." And then hastens to add, "I do not think it at all probable that aeronautics will ever come into play as a serious modification of transport and communication."

This was written one year before Kitty Hawk.

Wells estimated very well the future shape of war. He foresaw trench warfare with its stalemates — the consequences of the machine gun — and how they would give way in turn to aerial blitzkrieg. He foresaw the domination of war by science, and he states magnificently the central fact of the modern world:

The nation that produces in the near future the largest proportional development of educated and intelligent engineers and agriculturists, of doctors, schoolmasters, professional soldiers and intellectually active people of all sorts . . . will certainly be the nation that will be the most powerful in warfare as in peace, will certainly be the ascendant or dominant nation before the year 2000.

Later, in *The World Set Free* (1914), Wells even foresaw nuclear weapons and the possibility that they might make war impossible. He predicted that they would be achieved about 1940, which suggests that he was beginning to have a pretty good understanding of the gestation time for research and development. He was writing just a short time after the physicist Soddy had first conceived that the atomic energy in a cup of water could drive a ship across the Atlantic. ("That dreamer!" the other physicists called him. They were still calling him that in 1939.)

Yet we realize suddenly that Wells is not anticipating really new inventions at all, but only the consequences of things already done in his time. The airplane had already been foreshadowed by glider experiments and by Langley's model. Wells also foresaw helicopters, but in all his predictions before World War I, there is nothing like radar or jet propulsion or long-range rockets, all of which came within thirty years. There are no steel skyscrapers, no plastics, although they were almost upon him. In biology, Wells imagines growth hormones, perhaps seriously (*The Food of the Gods*, 1904), but nothing like vitamins or plasma; no new drugs or poisons like Salvarsan and penicillin and DDT; no new tools like radioactive tracers or the electron microscope.

Wells, the eager and speculative and successful, has also proved too tame for history.

LATER PROPHETS

After World War I, the prophets realized that they had to be bolder. But the story is much the same as before. We can group several forecasts together. Listen to Wells again, older and wiser, in *The Shape of Things to Come* (1932); and Aldous Huxley in *Brave New World* (1928); and J. B. S. Haldane in *The End of the World* (1923). In the next few hundred years (Haldane says the next few million), it seems we are to have helicopters and wrist-watch telephones or television. Clothes will be zippered, plastic, and disposable. Haldane has rocket space ships for colonizing other planets, and tidal and solar energy for moving mountain ranges and controlling climate.

In biology, life is to be prolonged and old age abolished. The unfit will be sterilized. People will be like full-page color ads, larger than life, aseptic, healthy, committing suicide only from airplanes. There will be new stimulants and new senses. New plants and animals created by artificial mutations. A Bureau of Hatchery and Conditioning producing children to order, with their minds carefully shaped for their destined roles. Promiscuity. "Everyone belongs to everyone else, now." A planned society, kept stable by incessant amusements.

Alas, these fantastic futures have a familiar ring, a sound not so different from the current headlines of the *New York Times*. They are here now, the wrist-watch phones, helicopters, moon rockets, wonder drugs, synthetic plants and animals. Solar energy has its millions for research; islands are destroyed and mountains moved by atomic bombs; manipulating the weather has become a big business. Mind-shaping and Miltown, artificial conception, promiscuity and the pressure of amusements, these brave new principles are old familiars to us. And atomic energy is not even in these particular forecasts, so that they were already surpassed by the first atomic pile in 1942. Today we transmute the immutable elements almost as routinely as we rearranged molecules when these prophets wrote.

After thirty years, the novel inventions that were to span the generations are rather well known already, at least in the embryo, and even their social effects are catching up with us. It looks as though our grandchildren of the year

2000 will go far beyond any of these predictions and will be as incomprehensible to us as the thought processes of William Jennings Bryan.

THE ELEMENTS OF PROPHECY

I think the errors in these forecasts were due not to a lack of imagination, but to a lack of analysis. They are not to be cured by making the prophecies wilder. This is the path down which science fiction has been increasingly driven. Prophecy becomes indistinguishable from fantasy and all connection with real live descendants disappears.

I think that for good forecasts, whether for a single industry or for all society, what we need is more realism, not less — the hardest-headed realism we can get. And we need a careful examination of the elements that make up a good prediction.

For example, it is of the first importance to avoid the kind of error Bellamy made. A prophecy can begin to take into account social forces and reforms only after it has calculated the technological future, and not before. Beside the inertia of our stubborn minds and our stubborn biology, devices now multiply so fast as to appear fluid. They pour in on us, acting in many little ways and by indirection to give a resultant force far more effective than the direct forces of resolves and crusades.

This is one of the main reasons why we need a new caste of prophets we can respect. The best political programs and legislation become dubious in the shadow of our ignorance about the technological future. It is the close contact with the greatness and uncertainty of irresistible evolutionary changes welling up unbidden and unknown — out of our technological subconscious, so to speak — that makes many scientists and engineers, even the "socially conscious" ones, feel that direct social or political action is fruitless unless it can work with these changes or take them into account. The brave new world comes true around us. Biology's great decade lies ahead. With this ferment rising, the most earnest frontal efforts in uplift or reform are like sand castles endangered by the tide. Research is the real revolution, a kind that no security questionnaire can ever detect and a thousand pulpits can never reverse.

An interesting corollary is that if technology drives society, society vulgarizes technology. This is Aldous Huxley's repeated point. The least cultural denominator is the first consequence of the mass market. The grand organ anthem on Bellamy's Utopian radio becomes a singing advertisement for liver pills. The degree of vulgarization of a device will be one of the hardest things to predict. It may depend on trivia, and on variables such as the methods of distribution. For example, in America, broadcast network radio has been more vulgar than wired music or hi-fi or books because it has had to reach a mass market to collect its fee. When good local FM stations took away the more selective part of the audience, it became more vulgar still; when television took away the less selective part, it improved. Evidently anyone who tries to prophesy the full social impact of an invention will have to understand the detailed nature of the individual feedbacks in a competitive situation, questions intimately connected with secondary technological tricks, economies, and legalisms.

But this is getting ahead of the primary question, which is the forecasting of technological developments themselves. This can be done successfully, I think, if three steps are clearly separated: the anticipation of inventions, the calculation of their development time and extent, and the estimation of their social consequences. Most persons will probably agree that the second and third of these steps can be accomplished if the first can be. Development times and markets, for example, are the natural province of vice-presidents and research directors; and a lively and sympathetic imagination will go a long way toward the estimation of social consequences. Starting from embryonic inventions, the prophets whom we have just looked at did these two steps very well, except for their absurdly long estimates of development times; and none of them had had any experience with industrial research. By contrast, a few of the American atomic scientists testified after World War II that Russia could develop her own atomic bomb in four to ten years — when generals were estimating thirty years, or never — and four years turned out to be correct. In 1948 I heard two well-known physicists making bets on whether man would reach the moon by 1960; today, three years after the first Sputnik, 1965 looks like a better target date. But for unbiased men, accuracy in such matters is a question of experience.

Developmental estimates of course must take into account the fact that every device and idea has its limits. Trains and automobiles reached their final cruising speeds within about forty years after they were invented. The mechanical theory of matter lasts a couple of generations and then gets superseded. Science and technology do not grow like a balloon, the same ball getting fuller of hot air; but like yeast, each bud reaching its limit and then new buds forming. By the time an idea has its Nobel prize, it is becoming exhausted. Only the new guesses and speculations that spring from it have any capacity for growth.

But the first step is the crucial one, the anticipation of

invention; and here we must note certain distinctions. Invention is not the same as discovery. And it is not to be confused with advances in the important basic research that good laboratories are always doing on perennial riddles. These three kinds of results, invention, discovery, and basic advances, differ considerably in their predictability. For example, discoveries are individually unpredictable. No one could have anticipated America, or X-rays or the electron. Collectively, however, they are predictable, in the sense that we know many useful discoveries will be made wherever men are busy exploring new fields.

Advances in the perennial riddles are harder to anticipate or assess. They give us new knowledge and new power, but it is a diffuse sort of power, sometimes instantly developed, sometimes delayed. Maxwell's equations led directly to the radio, but Einstein's did not lead at all directly to the atomic bomb. And today it seems unlikely that any new results on chromosomes or on visual perception, which has been studied for centuries, could remake society very fast. What social power these advances have depends mostly on their conversion into inventions men want.

WANTS AND INVENTIONS

Invention, on the other hand, is both predictable and immediately important to society. It is not necessary to be the inventor in order to see the general shape of things to come. In the first place, inventions as well as discoveries are not single but multiple, made simultaneously in many different places when the time is ripe. "There are now so many physicists that their behavior is becoming statistical," one of them has said. A technical development generally rests on, and is planned from, an older substratum of ideas and related work, just as the voyages of Columbus and Magellan were implicit in Eratosthenes. A group working in a field goes ahead in the general direction set by the work already done. Many of the discoveries they make, and most of the inventions, are therefore not accidental but almost unavoidable, and hence to a large extent foreseeable. As a result we can anticipate solutions to some degree just by looking at what is being worked on and what questions are being asked, even though the outsider and the insider alike may be unable to put together the final details for a long time.

Some research organizations now operate on such a large scale that the work of invention and even discovery can be programmed and can be partially turned over to an engineering development group. This shows us at the same time the second aspect of invention that makes it predictable. It is a social process, satisfying social wants. Whenever a highly concentrated research program gets under way, the technological improvements become limited not so much by what is possible or by what an Edison can think up as by what men desire. If a result is impossible one way, it is often possible another, and the only problem is to run through all the conceivable methods until the right one is found. In this real sense our conveniences and gadgets are simply wished into being, when we wish hard enough.

Men wished to fly, and they got balloons — fire balloons, gas balloons, and Zeppelins. They wished to fly without balloons. Four basically different devices have already appeared — the propeller plane, the helicopter, the jet plane and the rocket plane, involving three different motors. Such overlapping inventions might be even more nearly simultaneous if the appearance of the first success did not drain research energy for some time away from the other possibilities. To separate U-235, four different schemes were devised. All worked. Today we have not just one, but many different kinds of nuclear reactors and bombs and power plants.

As soon as a problem can be stated clearly, we are within a generation of solving it. Of course, the prophet must be careful. The new toy is not likely to be exactly what was expected and it may not be as useful as anticipated. Automatic dishwashers, unforeseen, can come and change our lives while we are still waiting for the moving sidewalks that many of the early oracles predicted. The new toy may also conflict with our other values; more crassly, we may refuse to pay the price for it. The coming of television, and now of color television, may have been somewhat delayed for this reason. Going to the moon is not a matter of physics, but of economics; the engineering advances that steadily make it easier are really advances in economy. And often when a fundamental restriction is encountered, we get around it by twisting our wants or rephrasing the question. We take an airplane instead of a flying carpet. The motion picture gives us many of the pleasures of the time machine and far less dangerously.

Nevertheless the fact that we are usually able to will into existence some approximation to our desires reduces the burden on the prophet of technology. The most important thing for him to do is to look realistically at what human beings want and need and will pay for; at what the research laboratories will move to after they have done what they are doing now; and at what the details are of cost, convenience and advantage, that determine the military, commercial, or private acceptability of new devices. Obviously he needs to know science inside and out, but within certain broad fundamental limits his central question is not so much "What are the scientists going to find?" — which is hard — but "What can we think of?" and "What do we want most?" and "How soon can it be ready?" — which are easier.

TOMORROW IN THE LABS

The laboratories are evidently at the focus of successful prophecy, technological or political. The really dramatic changes are often concentrated in a few minds, the Edisons and Pasteurs, and sometimes these men can even be identified after a little inquiry. Perhaps ten men in ten fields — the hot hundred — are the ones who determine in detail the shape of tomorrow. Oddly enough, even these, with their noses to the blackboard, do not always want to face the truth of how fast their latest pure theories will be transformed into daily necessities, or how fast new theory and inconceivable invention will be created.

One does not have to be a prophet to see that generally, barring catastrophe (whose form is also predictable and has a certain probability), the shape of the year 2000 must represent what the great laboratories are working on most intensely today. Their projects jump from the headlines, and it is not fantasy. To serve the doubled population of that time, with its doubled cities and doubled traffic and desperate expansion of birth control and conservation measures, atomic power will dominate the scene. There will be solar power. Probably fusion power. Planes and rockets everywhere, far more versatile and better controlled. Space travel. Ion propulsion. Fabulous metals and ceramics. New practical devices from fundamental nuclear physics. Remarkable understanding of molecules and of solids and liquids. A hundredfold better knowledge of the new experimental fields of astrophysics and of deep oceanography. Cheap, versatile communications, television everywhere. Fantastic slave devices, automatic control systems, computing machines for every kind of problem and policy, thinking machines, pattern-recognizing and learning machines. Accurate prediction and control of weather. In biology, the abolition of disease, the manipulation of species, and an understanding and control of heredity and growth such as we hardly dream of. Solutions to many of our great riddles — photosynthesis, vision, genetics, enzymes, antibodies, cancer. A hundredfold better understanding of the brain — that perennial problem that will never be finished.

And I see the laboratories turning to many problems almost untouched today. New batteries and portable fuels for vehicles. A fundamental rethinking of clothing and shelter. Farming the oceans. Professor R. L. Meier recently listed twenty-six basic research problems connected with our present population explosion which are not being worked on today. These and many related problems should become major lines of effort in a few years, if industry really understands its own long-range interests. The maldistribution of scientists across all these different fields, with thousands in some areas and a handful in others, is proof, if any were needed, that research and invention is a social process, easily turned in any direction of wants and profits.

AS DEEP AS MYTH

It would be interesting for an organized forecasting group to work out the details of these predictions of the world for forty or so years ahead. But to make any longer-range prophecy, it is clear that they would have to aim at the really distant steps, the unbelievable steps, of the technological sequence. The believable we do in this generation; the conceivable in the next. The third generation we do not understand.

To estimate such far-off invention, I can only conclude from this analysis that within very broad limits, the best guide is not going to be a technical guide at all, but simply the knowledge of what men really and deeply want. Today the limitations on the development of science and invention in the foreseeable future seem to be set only loosely by nature, more tightly by the abilities of exceptional minds, but most tightly of all by the human desire and its balance of values. The intricacy of problems we can eventually solve, the complexity of communications we can organize and the amount of power we can control are vast beyond imagining. Very nearly, we will go where we wish and make what we will.

Among our many desires, the most powerful are the simple ones. I cannot help thinking that the dominant fact over the long run is therefore going to be the steady pressure of elementary desires in shaping the kind of inventions we generate and accept, and the kind of societies we thereby create. To be warm and full and free, these are our first needs, the needs that can erupt in violent revolution, but they are not all. What dissolves and remolds societies unawares is that we also want, like children, to have sweet smells, music, pictures, entertainment, bright lights, and powerful servants. We want to make magic, to run like the wind and fly like the birds and talk across the miles and be as beautiful as gods and know how everything works. In the Western World, I think these longings are part of a deeper dream of godlike power itself. Prometheus, Daedalus, Frankenstein, Faust — there is psychological and racial truth for our questioning Greek minds in the dark power myths of human technical mastery stolen from heaven. This scientific age is the very time of their surging up and fulfillment and they burst daily into reality among us. It is the edge of creation we skirt, recombining the genes and the viruses. Our monsters twitch, almost alive, as the antennae, the sense organs and reflexes, the electronic brains and computers, of planes and ships and guided missiles become ever more animate.

The most sophisticated science moves to the service of deep and ancient dreams. In atomic energy, many have found a kind of re-enactment of the Faustian drama of power and damnation. Some people today seem to pull their mental skirts back in horror from nuclear scientists as they once shrank fascinated from black magic or the hooded alchemist. With better reason: the alchemists did not dream boldly enough. Was ever the imagined transmutation of lead into gold — that petty relic of savage trade! — even a fraction so overwhelming as that of uranium to plutonium, which never was on land or sea, and then plutonium into everything? Even the names give the nightmare dream away: Uranus, god of heaven; and Pluto, death. And today we fly up to the very spheres on which the old gods moved.

To be accurate over the long run, the prophets of society

will have to speak the language of technology, but they will have to dream as deep as myth. In the past, the serious ones have shrunk from such simplicity. They have spoken of what men can do, not of what they will to do. So their predictions have suffered always from a lack of realistic imagination. The mad dreamers were evidently not mad enough. It is time for some madder realists to learn to prophesy.

5. THE FIFTH NEED: NOVELTY

WE SOMETIMES ask ourselves what are the essential external needs of man, the needs that must be supplied if his body is to continue life at all. The usual answers are four: air, water, food, and in severe climates, protection. But it is becoming clear today that the human organism has one other absolute necessity. It is one that has not been much emphasized in the past, probably because even in the arctic or in the desert, on high mountains or in dungeons, we have rarely been deprived of it entirely. We could scarcely appreciate the anguish that deprivation would cause or the subtle and numerous ways in which this commodity normally contributes to our well-being. This fifth need is the need throughout our waking life for a continuous novelty and variety of external stimulation of our eyes, ears, sense organs and all our nervous network.

These days the word novelty suggests a cheap plastic toy, the sort of thing that appeals to children, that is played with for a moment and then gets forgotten and stepped on in the rush to some newer excitement. Childish curiosity is one part of my meaning. But I use novelty also to mean a wider search for the continually new. Several lines of evidence now suggest that such a search goes on in the human organism from babyhood to old age and from our simplest acts of perception to our loftiest intellectual achievements. Our brains organize, and exist to organize, a great variety of incoming sensory messages every waking second, and can become not only emotionally upset but seriously deranged if these messages cease or even if they cease to be new. New experience is not merely a childish want; it is something we cannot do without. Our demand for it is a driving force of the greatest importance in both our personal and social activities. I think it is interesting to explore a little the nature of this demand and to see how very far its influence may extend.

When I use the word "novelty" in describing it, it is true that I have in mind a more precise idea. In the field of information theory, developed in the last decade from the work of Shannon and Wiener and others, the messages that flow into and out of a communications system are said to carry more or less "information." The word has taken on mathematical and technical overtones that it does not have in common usage. Warren Weaver explains it this way:

> Information is . . . a measure of one's freedom of choice in selecting a message. The greater this freedom of choice [for the sender], and hence the greater the information, the greater is the uncertainty [for the receiver] that the message actually is a particular one. Thus greater freedom of choice, greater uncertainty, greater information go hand in hand.

Conversely, when there is complete certainty as to what the message will be, it carries no information. Nothing is as obsolete as yesterday's newspaper. It is only good to wrap fish in, precisely because it no longer carries information. What I am calling the fifth need of man is the need for information in this sense, for a continuous, novel, unpredictable, a nonredundant and surprising flow of stimuli into the human brain. I do not mean just a series of flickering lights, of course, or a madman's chatter. This might be infinitely surprising, but would not interest us very long. Our sense impressions obviously must be organized into meaningful patterns if they are to bring us much information in either the common or the technical sense. But the most important pattern of all is the pattern of change.

In a general way it has always been known that men need change. Put a man in a box, and he goes nuts. But the recent laboratory experiments on sensory deprivation have nevertheless been rather startling in their revelation of just how this happens. Almost everyone has now read about these psychological studies in which volunteers were put in isolation rooms with softly bandaged heads and hands, or were floated in warm swimming pools where they could touch nothing and could see only dimness and hear only a low hum. It was not a vacation, as some might think! The men found they lost the sense of time, could not remember things or concentrate, had wild hallucinations and finally could not even add or subtract. They were healthy normal men, comfortable, with no alcohol or drugs, and they saw little yellow demons marching across the desert carrying enormous sacks. If the loudspeaker in the room finally asked a question or made a statement, it was the happiest of sounds. Yes, of course, two and two make seven, if the loudspeaker thought so. There was deeper truth in that, touching all philosophy.

After a couple of days of this, every one of the men came staggering out, having thought about nothing they had planned to think about, unable to answer simple questions, and refusing to go back at any price. Stir-crazy.

And for hours after they took off the bandages, the walls seemed to weave in and out. Dreams were strange and it was days before perception and problem-solving returned to normal.

These experiments seem to prove, if any proof were needed, that our bodies and brains are not made to operate in a vacuum. The highest intellectual activities require continual little corrections and reassurances from the outside world. Secretaries cannot work in offices that are too well soundproofed. Tests on animals show that they also have the need for continual variety in some degree. Their responses and problem-solving abilities become permanently and seriously defective if they do not get the full range of normal stimulation almost from the moment of birth. We have all heard of neglected or institutional children who show similar deficiencies. As we shall see, there are various other bits of evidence bearing on why a human or animal nervous system may require a continuous input of information in order to function normally, but it is clear that, however it is to be explained, the need itself is real and vital.

In many ways, the demand is like the demand for food. There can be a level of starvation and a level of gluttony. At the jail level, men wolf down their bread or soup, but will sometimes sacrifice a little of that, even, for a glimpse of the sky or a crumb of gossip. At higher and more normal levels of information flow, the need is relaxed and we can afford discrimination and rich creative enjoyment, gourmets of mental fare. It is no accident that we speak of intellectual preferences as "taste." And, as with food, we sometimes overload our networks with stimulation until we get mental bellyaches and can no longer absorb any more. The crying of an overexcited child is not so different from that of an overstuffed one. At all levels, the mental and physical appetites are equally real and equally imperious.

But to call this a need for "information," is not that just dressing up the obvious in fashionable pedantry? Those are certainly not new ideas, someone will say. The wise have always known that man does not live by bread alone. True enough. But the old wisdom often strikes us with greater force by being fitted into the framework of our own time. I think it is surprising to see how bright a light the notation of information-demand throws into many strange corners of human behavior. It brings into relief the nature of boredom and of humor, of gambling and of learning, of our aesthetic judgments and creative behavior in art and music, and of the driving forces behind social revolutions.

These are broad claims, I know. Is this just an attempt to force everything to fit one pet formula? I think not. If we are really dealing with one of the fundamental needs of man, absolutely essential to our normal functioning minute by minute, then it should touch every aspect of life. The areas I have mentioned are just a few where it is easy to show how dramatically pertinent this notion is. They encompass some of our most characteristically human behavior. Man is said to be the only animal that laughs. He may also be the only one that gambles. The strength of our devouring demand for novelty and surprise could almost be said to be at the root of our differences from the higher animals.

In a moment we will come to the question of how this need for novelty can be explained, but it is interesting to see first how many scholars and critics have already emphasized the role of "information" in high human behavior. Many of them did not call it "information," of course, but the general idea, that a desire for the unpredictable and surprising is central to our intellectual activities, crops up again and again.

AESTHETICS AND INFORMATION

Take aesthetic criticism, for example. My colleague, Professor Leonard Meyer of our Department of Music at the University of Chicago, has recently written a book, *Emotion and Meaning in Music,* in which he puts forward a theory of musical aesthetics that has been well received in many circles. Professor Meyer argues as follows. Music or any other symbolic art may have two kinds of "meaning" for the hearer or observer. One is its denotative meaning, where the music refers to some experience outside itself, either by obvious imitation or by accepted convention. The *Household Symphony* amuses us because of its domestic noises, and minor keys are poignant in the Western World because we sing sad songs to them. But formal music is dominated by an inherent meaning, in which the only meaning is a purely musical one. It is the latter with which Meyer is concerned in his theory.

We all know that we can and do enjoy certain sequences of quite abstract sounds, patterns of pulsation of the air that are almost devoid of human content. What makes them enjoyable? Meyer says that what happens is that, when we listen to music:

> We are, in a sense, constantly expecting. Under certain conditions we expect change, under others continuity, and under still others, repetition; until finally we expect the

conclusion of the piece. Thus in a very general way expectation is always ahead of the music, creating a background of diffuse tension against which particular delays articulate the affective cause and create meaning. Formal expectation is constantly active on several architectonic levels as a sort of generalized aesthetic tension which is shaped and particularized in the course of listening.

Meyer suggests that the inherent musical meaning, the emotional as well as the intellectual satisfaction, lies just in this expectation and in the composer's manipulation of our tensions, by turns subtly thwarted or subtly satisfied, as the music develops. The expectations are not the same for a new piece as for a familiar one, of course. In sufficiently serious music they may change with each rehearing, until finally we see that the whole piece satisfies far larger expectations than we had at first.

Take "Three Blind Mice," a simple tune but one that may have lasted for centuries. "Three blind mice. Three blind mice." Dull, isn't it, by the second repetition? Does it dare repeat again? No. Once more exactly the same and it would be just a broken record. The repetition does come, satisfying us, but at a higher pitch, teasing us. "See how they run, see how they run." Ah, double again. Now we see the larger pattern. There should be a third double repetition, perhaps "They ran away, they ran away," at a still higher pitch. No, there shouldn't. That would make it just another piano exercise. The song breaks into a frolic, a new theme; and it is repeated not two times, but three, surprising us again; and then with a thump we are round the circle and back at the beginning with those solemn "Three blind mice" once more.

Delightful surprises, from three to five! But they do not hold us for many years. Finally we are seven and sophisticated. It takes variations on the variations now to keep our interest. The process of redefining banality and re-enlarging our capacity of expectation goes on up year by year to the most advanced and intricate musical structures.

I think this peek-a-boo delight in being fooled and pleased and fooled and pleased again is essentially our delight in the flow of new "information" into our nervous system. Beethoven is better than bop because he is less redundant. But Meyer emphasizes that our satisfaction in music is not due to complexity alone. The most barbarous noises can be complex. It is due to our "understanding" of the complexity, our ability to anticipate with the help of our musical experience the echoes and analogies that finally show themselves as the grand pattern is completed.

When we do not know what to expect, as when we listen to Oriental music for the first time, we are equally surprised by everything and so are surprised by nothing. The music carries no information to us, in the technical sense of contradicting our expectations, because we have none. It brings us no meaning and Meyer says this is why it brings us no emotion, except a desire to get out. Mozart's genius, it is said, was that he combined the maximum of surprise with the maximum of inevitability.

We are as unhappy at the other end of the scale, when our expectations are simple and perfectly fulfilled. When Junior plays "Three Blind Mice" on his little machine for the fifteenth time, whatever architectonic novelty is still being developed for him is not being developed for his mother, and she screams "Stop that! You're driving me crazy!"

Professor Meyer later comes to point out the possible connection of his theory with information theory, "the importance of uncertainty in musical communication, the probabilistic nature of musical style." He concludes, "It would seem that the psycho-stylistic conditions which give rise to musical meaning, whether affective or intellectual, are the same as those which communicate information."

Meyer's theory is interesting here because it is so explicit in showing the role that the fifth need may play in our behavior. But the relation of aesthetic satisfaction to expectation and surprise was recognized in several fields long before the development of information theory. We can find it in the early poetic criticism of T. S. Eliot:

> The most interesting verse which has yet been written in our language has been done either by taking a very simple form, like the iambic pentameter, and constantly withdrawing from it, or taking no form at all, and constantly approximating to a very simple one. It is this contrast between fixity and flux, this unperceived evasion of monotony, which is the very life of verse.

Is not this the same idea again, in different words? See how similar also is Coleridge's description of the nature of the creative imagination. He says it "reveals itself in the balance or reconcilement of opposite or discordant qualities . . . the sense of novelty and freshness, with old and familiar objects . . ." And so on.

Eliot even seems to feel the need of a new term to describe this essential principle in poetry. He says in one place: "Poetry is a superior amusement: I do not mean an amusement for superior people . . . If we think of the nature of amusement, then poetry is not amusing; but if we think of anything else that poetry may seem to be, we are led into far greater difficulties." And he rejects several other classic definitions, saying they are "frigid to anyone who has felt the full surprise and elevation of a new experience of poetry."

This careful use of the terms "amusement" and "surprise" seems to me to refer exactly to constantly changing expectations and unexpected fulfillments; that is, to "information" in our technical sense. (In discussing the Great Tradition in poetry, Eliot even extends to all of history this basic notion of expectation crossed by change.) I am not trying to force all criticism into this formula. I know that other definitions of poetry express important truths. It is not my aim to intrude in these intramural debates except as an appreciative observer of the unities. All I want to point out is that "information" is evidently one of the recognized aesthetic elements, and one that may be as important for the formal aspects of poetry as it is for the formal aspects of music.

Eliot uses the term "amusement," and Cleanth Brooks has written of "The Language of Paradox" in poetry. This suggests that we might take a look at the bearing of the fifth need on a different field, the field of humor. Many deep and humorless analyses have been made of why we laugh. But everyone knows that we laugh at the unexpected, provided it is in a deeper sense expected and right. The dignified man who slips on a banana peel. The comedian who repeats the punch line like a musical theme three times, but changes it a little the third time to mean something quite different, making us laugh the loudest of all. Is "information" not at the root of humor also?

What is wit but inevitability and surprise? "The mass of men lead lives of quiet desperation." Who would have thought of "desperation"? Or of "quiet" with it? And who can deny them? We cannot forget it in a hundred years. "A common language divides England and America." "All the deadly virtues plague my death." The line we remember is the one with the most concentrated information. The expected unexpected, the double meaning, completing a deeper architectonic pattern.

In fact it is startling to realize that it is formal music that may show us humor in its purest form, completely divorced from external or imitative reference. Everyone has experienced purely musical surprises, that made a whole audience laugh on cue. In the light of Meyer's theory, such behavior almost amounts to a proof that any theory of laughter hereafter will have to start from an analysis of formal expectation in an information sequence. If musical audiences were more homogeneous in their experience and expectations, they might laugh at many twists in the composition that now give them only a diffuse pleasure.

But we tire of the same joke, whether musical or visual or verbal, we tire of the joker if heard too often, and finally we tire of the whole style. A current headline says "Can TV Comedians Last?" The answer is, No, not without a continuous variation of style, and then a variation of the variation, fast enough to keep ahead of public sophistication. We cannot step into the same joke twice. Humor is only relative to our continually changing expectations. There is no such thing as an absolutely funny remark.

VARIETY AND ITS ROLE IN LEARNING

Why this insatiable thirst for novelty? To some students of human learning and information-handling, it now seems that the demand for variety may be built in, that it may be a necessary aspect of the way our nervous systems grow and operate.

Several lines of evidence suggest this. One is the importance of learning in man, with its concomitant need of an external variety to be learned from. An insect apparently does not learn. As soon as it emerges from its pupa, it knows how to find its particular kind of food or how to build its complex particular nest. This implies a rigid and predetermined nervous system, with the fixed responses we might expect from a complicated little electronic computer.

The birds, higher up the scale, show a fascinating mixture of predetermined and learned behavior. Many can learn songs or even human speech. Lorenz showed that they learn who their mothers are, by "imprinting" the nearest large moving object, sometime in the first twenty-four hours after hatching. This has amusing results if the object is a man or a red wagon. ("Mary Had a Little Lamb" shows the same phenomenon in sheep.) But a bird hatched in isolation knows, without learning, how to find the normal food of its species or how to build a normal nest or to exhibit normal courting behavior.

On the other hand, learning comes to play a dominant role in the higher mammals and in human beings. This means that a major part of our nervous systems must not be predetermined at birth but must grow in some way almost continuously throughout life under the impact of external stimulation and experience. The network may finally be able to play Bach and to pilot planes, responding quickly and accurately to experiences that never happened to any ancestor. It takes weeks for the bird to learn its song, but years for the child to learn tennis or the piano. The need to complete the connections in this large non-predetermined section of our brains may be the major reason for our long childhood and apprenticeship before we reach full adult mental and muscular competence. It is a tremendous evolutionary step for the individual to be able to go so far beyond the instructions contained in the egg; and we may be only at the beginning of this development. But already, it seems we have in ourselves a learning machine designed to be faced with continually new things to learn.

A second line of evidence comes from the experiments that show we need moment-by-moment variety in order to perceive anything, and stage-by-stage variety throughout childhood in order to comprehend anything. At the level of simple perception, the ear becomes deaf to a continuous tone, and the eye is now found to require continual little tremor movements in order to see anything. These movements are so tiny and quick that we cannot detect them except with instruments, but they produce a continual comparison of one part of the visual field with another and so produce a continual change in the illumination of each visual cell, which is evidently necessary for vision. What we perceive is only what varies. What we see is not objects, but relationships.

Hebb at Montreal and his school of psychologists have emphasized further that many of the environmental relationships that seem almost self-evident to us as adults were in fact learned at a very early age. For example, a number of adults have been operated on to remove cataracts that had kept them blind from birth. But it was found that, even after their sight had been made normal by all optical tests, it still took weeks before they could tell a key lying on the table from a book, except by touch. They could not distinguish a triangle from a square visually except by laboriously counting the corners. At some stage in their blinded childhood, when they should have been learning fast and accurate key-book distinctions and triangle-square distinctions, their perceptual networks must have been making useless and irrelevant connections, like a chick with no mother to be imprinted to. The visual geometry they are trying to learn as adults is superimposed on a wrong and tangled foundation. It is as though their brains had been processing and storing information all the time regardless of whether it was good or bad information, straight or crazy.

Likewise with animals. Puppies have been kept isolated for various periods of time in a lighted but windowless and featureless box, with feeding and cleaning being done by hidden apparatus. If released after six months, they are perceptibly more stupid than normal dogs. If released after eighteen months, they are far more stupid. Years later, they still have puppy behavior, insatiably curious, learning poorly, frisking in again and again to the same shock or unpleasant experience. The lack of normal variety at the proper stages in their early environment has stunted their minds as much as the lack of physical space in the box would have stunted their bodies. The adult human subjects who went without variety for a few days had only a taste of this distortion, but it was real. The mind's need for various and structured experience to organize is evidently present in adults as well as infants, and probably is present all through life.

Further evidence that the demand for information is

built in is provided by measurements on the rate of operation of the human brain in various respects. Just physio-
logically, the brain uses a tremendous fraction, 20 to 25
per cent, of the blood and oxygen supply of the resting
body. No one has found any direct connection between
this and our mental work, but it does suggest that the brain
is a most important organ, to be kept in operation all the
time at a high rate of activity. More pertinent are the direct measurements by Miller and by Quastler and others on
the information-processing rate of human beings. They
wanted to find out how complicated an instrument panel
a pilot can watch without making mistakes. It turns out
that no matter what kind of signals are fed to him, flashing
lights or dials or even verbal instructions, his total capacity
for handling the information is roughly constant, like the
capacity of a water pipe of a certain diameter through which
only so much water can flow per second. And probably his
information-handling capacity and ours remains the same,
no matter whether the signals are given by a psychologist
or are those of our normal waking life. Every source of
external stimulation is grist for the mill. At every waking
instant it seems that the brain must be paying attention
to something, processing some kind of new information,
whether it is the twitch of a skirt or the organization of a
field campaign, or both together. Attention wanders; but
it is not shut off except by sleep.

Of course we must not be misled into supposing that
our brains manipulate this sensory information in the same
way that an insect or an electronic computer or even an
elaborate self-guiding missile does. To say that we learn
describes the difference inadequately. Our whole mode of
operation is different. This shows in many ways. Our

brains and others of the higher mammals search for structure and pattern in the environment. They have "closure"
— the ability to fill in a gap in the pattern — so that they
can reach a correct conclusion in spite of a missing piece of
evidence that would stop a computer or send it in circles.
They can anticipate events that they have never experienced.

The higher brains reason by clues and analogies. They
break up problems into parts familiar enough to be solved
separately. They use symbols, which express the naked es-
sence of analogy, and tools, the visible physical expression
of analogy. Many definitions have been made for man: that
he is the talking animal, the tool-using animal, the time-
binding animal, the only animal that laughs. I suspect they
all grow out of his uniquely developed way of processing
and organizing and learning new information. And that
our continuous information demand is just another expression of the same organizational principle, whatever it may
be, which an insect or an electronic computer does not
have.

In any case, all the evidence points to the fact that a brain
is constructed to consume input information as a stomach
consumes food, only more continuously and throughout
life.

THE SEARCH FOR VARIETY

If the fifth need drives individuals, it drives societies too.
How many of our social wheels are turned, not by our material needs for food and drink, but simply by our demand
for new stimulation!

The passion for gambling is made to order for any theory

of human behavior that gives the demand for "information" a central place. It was the turn of the cards and the dice and the wheel that produced the science of statistics, which is the mathematical basis of information theory. If anyone has been reluctant to believe with Professor Meyer that the mere input of "information" or surprise can generate emotion, he has only to look at gamblers. The emotion is obviously connected with the uncertainty more than with the losing or gaining of money, whether pence or pounds, because when we gain or lose money in more certain ways the fascination and the passion disappear. Games of chance have always had more devotees than games of complete information such as checkers or chess. It is hard to be quantitative about it, but if we add up racing and football pools and the other betting sports, the numbers game, dice and bingo and bridge and poker and slot machines and luxury gambling, we might find them a large fraction of the total leisure time expenditures of modern societies. I fail to see how this particular mode of behavior can be specifically accounted for by any of the traditional psychological drives. It is the clearest indicator there could possibly be that there is a demand in human beings to consume the unexpected.

We could go on to a dozen other social activities dominated by the same demand. It is trivial to say that what the entertainment industry sells is variety. Chess and vandalism are artificial ways of generating novelty. It is the latest that we welcome, in literature, in clothing and in housing. Detroit spends hundreds of millions a year to create a difference in cars where no difference exists. The automobile itself with its opportunities for speed and tourism, for leaving the humdrum neighborhood behind every morning — is not most of our need for it simply the demand for variety in our experiences? When the ideal factory constructs an ideal garden town around itself so that the employees can walk to work, it finds in a little while that vast numbers of them live miles away to avoid seeing the same old gang by night as by day.

Some might say this craze for change is peculiar to America or to countries of advanced technology. But a little examination shows that it is present in all races and cultures. The new technology has simply provided the means to satisfy it faster. In fact it is often the inexperienced peoples who are most hypnotized by movies and television. The successive waves of jazz, bop, rock-and-roll find converts in every country they touch. Everyone wants change. In France, Coca-Cola encroaches on wine at the very instant when, in America, wine seems to be encroaching on Coca-Cola.

What is the "alternation of generations" but a demand for something different? The energetic young will seek for anything,

> Some to the wars, to try their fortune there;
> Some to discover islands far away;
> Some to the studious universities . . .

just so they will not have to spend their youth at home. And the sons of these energetic ones may then make any compromise to have stable and settled lives instead. It has often been said that wars are brought on by boredom as much as by fanaticism or ambition. The leaders of the thirties did not assemble their Youth Movements by promises of sex and loot so much as by the prospect of new challenges, new roles and new excitements. It made an irresistible appeal to the children of civil servants.

I think that for any society hereafter to be stable against

revolutions or adventurers, it must provide for the young a tremendous input of continuously new stimulation so that they can satisfy their desire for variety in harmless ways. In this limited sense the Roman emperors were wise when they said the recipe for stability was bread and circuses. The demand for variety had to be filled no less than the demand for food. Today it would be television instead of circuses. We speak of the apathy of the young; perhaps it is the stabilizing effect of the flickering screens. After the vicarious nightly adventure, daytime meandering seems less pressing.

This was the purpose of the continuous amusement that Aldous Huxley described in *Brave New World*. He imagined that it could and would create a social stability that is in many ways more frightening than the suppression in George Orwell's society of 1984. Naked suppression is an open invitation to revolution. If not today, tomorrow. The human spirit is crushed but still explosive. In Huxley's nightmare, on the other hand, the finest and most revolutionary minds are simply diverted into isolated or pointless challenges.

But I suspect that there is no absolute security against our demand for novelty. A repetitious amusement ceases to be amusing. Sooner or later even Huxley's type of world would find its administrative apparatus penetrated from within by reformers determined to make some deeper change in the structure itself, as though their lives depended on it. I think the most unified and beneficent world government will find itself divided to the death from time to time. In every generation energetic men want to bet their lives on something. The placid times are when they bet on mountain-climbing or skin-diving rather than on revolution.

This leads me to think that the only really stable society will be a "progressive" society, a society continually stimulated by new information, so that it does not have to relieve recurrent boredom with recurrent crusades or circuses. The West has been so, exploring continually new frontiers of geography, of religion and science and the mind. I think this is both a need and a good. Better Socrates dissatisfied than a pig satisfied. I want Socrates dissatisfied, Athens dissatisfied, a world dissatisfied. "Man is a bridge and not a goal; and an arrow of longing for the further shore." Society cannot be stable; but the most stable society will be founded on the moving rock of "Progress Forever."

For there is no limit to the fifth need. After novelty must come a novel novelty. Bertrand Russell has discussed what he calls the love of excitement. He says that excitement, along with ambition, rivalry, vanity, and love of power, is one of "the infinite desires" of men which can never be satisfied, and that it represents a social energy unconsidered by moralists and social reformers. These other desires seem to represent some kind of mixture of a need for security with the need for novelty. The need for novelty helps give them their infinite character, for security alone could be satisfied easily if it did not keep questioning itself.

But it is the love of excitement that represents the fifth need in its purest form. And the social energy that Russell says it generates is one thing that gives me hope for the world. We can see this fermenting energy in children as they watch television over the years. At the age of seven, they force their mothers to buy the cereals advertised. At ten they want more excitement than that old stuff, and they turn off the commercials themselves. But nothing is more redundant than a stock comedian or a Western film.

In a few years, after they have been bored by all the adventure stories and all the detective stories and all the singers and gagsters, I think that a few of them will turn off the set altogether. Yes, they know what they hate. Some of them — not many, but some — finally will want a quiet room where they can look in their own minds for problems that are "deep and hard and new," as Oppenheimer says; a variety of experience that the little screen can never offer. They will write bizarre novels or transformation equations. A few will establish coteries to proclaim their difference, and then new dissenters will break away from that monotony too. Riesman argues that higher education should be systematically "counter-cyclical," deliberately opposing the standard banalities of the world outside at any given moment, so as to encourage in intelligent students this quest for variety that refreshes and stimulates the whole social structure.

The coteries — will they always find something important to challenge or create? I think so. Every new medium — even television — will attract creative minds, and after these, new minds to create something different, and so on repeatedly, generating the historical tradition that Eliot describes; until the whole space of opportunities available for creation has been staked out and all the minor niches have been filled. Then some new arena will offer more and will attract the most creative minds, and the process will repeat itself all over again.

The fifth need, the need for novelty at every level of experience, is a necessary part of the human organism. I think there is little danger that we can ever descend for long to the uniform and repetitious frivolity of *Brave New World*. Our demands are infinite. The search for the unexpected has given us the variety of frontiers and challenges that we have today, a greater variety than ever before. As long as the race endures, creative minds will continue to reach out from the familiar variety of their fathers to the highest intellectual challenges they are capable of.

6. PLAIN TALK ABOUT INTELLIGENCE

THE DIFFERENCES in the looks and the behavior of human beings have always been a marvel to me. I remember that when I was growing up in Florida, there was one man in our community, a good man, who looked like a gorilla. He had long hairy arms and a barrel chest and when he laughed, which was often, it was a coarse furniture-rattling laugh such as I imagined a gorilla might make if he had been given the power of laughter.

Later when I went off to college, my sensitivity to the varieties of appearance and character had been sharpened. I began to see many men whom it amused me to classify privately as resembling one bright-eyed animal or another. In the course of some years of university teaching, I have known and liked one tarsier well, and a great Dane and a couple of bullfrogs; and there was one favorite vegetable professor who looked like an unmade bed and talked like a pillow. Of course I suspect that, like the fellow in the song about the Eddystone Light, after you have counted the porpoise and the porgy, the other is me; and I probably look like some queer animal, too, I won't guess what, pedaling off down 58th Street with what hair I have left stuck out akimbo in the wind.

But the remarkable thing about it is that among men who really know something, the looks quickly cease to matter. I remember very clearly the dinner party where I first met L. L. Thurstone, the engineer who became a psychologist and developed the powerful statistical method called factor analysis. At first I thought he was one of the homeliest men I had ever seen. I have a memory of piercing eyes, and ears like sails, and a nose that seemed to have grown at random. But within ten seconds after he began to talk, I could no longer see the face at all, for I was looking at a mind. The excitement of hearing his reasoning and his experience led the whole party out into an area of intellect where such trivia as looks and clothes, the room, the dinner, all faded into the background. I think we rose not knowing what we had eaten and had brandy afterwards not knowing what we were drinking, we were so wrapped up in the flow of the conversation. I suppose it was painful to our hostess that we did not notice much her careful preparations; but if I have forgotten her entrée, I have not forgotten her guest of honor.

Around a good university, the minds are the realest things there are. And after a little while you realize that it is not only in our external looks that we resemble various strange unkempt animals, but in the shapes of our intellects, too. Each has its peculiar distortion. The mental ears stick out; the brain has its own hairy and primitive arms. But I think I also see the shapes of many wonderful new patterns of mind that cannot any longer be compared even fancifully to animals because they are types that have scarcely existed in the world before.

It is interesting to look at these gross differences in the kinds of intelligence and at the new races of mind that may be slowly evolving among us, like the intellectual fingers of mankind reaching and spreading out to unknown ends.

MALE AND FEMALE

There are three kinds of mental difference that impress me most, the difference between men and women, between genius and stupidity, and between different creative talents. The differences between the minds of men and women are numerous, and we often joke about them. If a man's car hits a laundry truck and he phones his wife about it, the first thing she asks is the name of the laundry. Are such differences in outlook innate, a matter of a sexual difference in brain physiology and organization? Or are they cultural, imposed perhaps in childhood by the different expectations and behavior of the adults in our society toward the growing boy and girl?

For example, are men dominant and women submissive? Not necessarily innately. Matriarchal cultures ruled by women have flourished for centuries. Europeans and Philip Wylie even say that America is a matriarchy in which the dominance of women is simply expressed in covert ways.

Do girls hate technical subjects and boys love them? Not necessarily innately. Girls get dolls. Boys get Erector sets. No wonder the girls often dislike the angularities of ruler and compass later. I do not know what toys the Russians give their girl children, but most of their doctors and 30 per cent of their scientists are women, a fraction many times greater than in America. Their numerical excess of scientists and engineers over ours is principally due to these numbers of women.

But I can mention two fields, music and poetry, where there is roughly equal social opportunity for both sexes to show their abilities and where real differences still seem to appear. Who takes the most music lessons in America?

Girls. Which sex predominates in teaching music? Women. Up through high school there are plenty of girls in the school orchestras. A woman composer would not be frowned upon.

But who plays the piano spontaneously in the Student Union Lounge? Always boys. Among adults, which sex composes? Which sex gets together for chamber music? Men. I would be glad to be convinced otherwise, but it seems to me that women may not have the musical *vocation*, except for a talented few.

Likewise in poetry. There are women poets, and good ones. But I do not think they give the reader the sense of mastery. And today I see no discrimination, either by publishers or readers, against women authors, who are legion; yet the number of serious women poets is very much less than the number of men.

I admire intellectual women. They represent a source of power that is kept under wraps in our society by our romantic ideas of work and marriage. The power is frittered away in bridge and Benefits when it might have revolutionized medicine and remade cities. But even if they were released from these invisible chains, I think the women who have a real vocation for abstract creations such as music and poetry might still be rare.

The male dominance in these fields resembles somewhat the male dominance in certain hereditary disorders, such as colorblindness and hemophilia, which women sometimes do have, but much less frequently. Such disorders are said to be due to a sex-linked recessive gene. I have a whimsical notion that the male brilliance in abstract creation may be a sex-linked recessive disorder of the mind. The genetic make-up of women may tend to stabilize them against this disease and make them principally "carriers" of it, as they are of colorblindness.

Of course, today we know that genetics is just the beginning of the difference between the sexes. The concentration of certain drugs in the body can strongly affect mental behavior in various ways, but the sex hormones are particularly powerful. Rats, male or female, injected with a trace of male hormone at a certain spot in the brain, come out fighting; with a trace of female hormone at another spot, they want to mother everything in sight. The survival of the species must often have depended on this sensitivity to our internal chemical balance. When such questions are understood better, we may come to know what are the "normal" mental and behavioral differences between the chemistries of the sexes, and how they vary with the changes in our bodies during growth and love and parenthood and old age. Some day, even a "masculine" interest in abstract creation may be turned on and off like a faucet by taking the proper hormone.

GENIUS AND STUPIDITY

The second big difference between human minds is far more obvious than the sexual differences, but is harder to discuss, because many of its more personal aspects are — and perhaps should be — socially taboo. Yet I think it is time for scientists and others to say aloud bluntly and clearly their various views on this matter, because our success as a democracy and indeed many aspects of our future welfare and happiness now depend on understanding it correctly.

The dreadful secret is that men differ greatly in intelligence.

We all know this, of course, in a general way. You are
not an Einstein and neither am I. Many of us have taken
tests and have found out our own Intelligence Quotients,
or our children's. Naturally they make our blood pressure
rise, and we are sure the tests are wrong — whether they
show us to be feeble-minded 80's or average 100's or man-
agerial 130's. You cannot go around comparing I.Q.'s with
your friends and fellow workers, unless you want to lose
them all. This is why the subject is tricky to discuss.

As a result, many psychologists today dislike the use of
the I.Q. They say it is somewhat uncertain, that it arouses
these emotional reactions, and that it stresses verbal and
mathematical problem-solving abilities and neglects other
valuable abilities in a person. Nevertheless, the things I
have to say will be understood best if we keep the I.Q. scale
in mind. It is the only index in general use that measures
even roughly the tremendous differences in the analytical
mental abilities of students and men. These differences are
the dominant fact of life in the physical sciences and, I
think, in every area where analytical brilliance is important.
We may not need to know them individually or invidiously,
but there are some social problems that we cannot understand or attack sensibly unless we know them at least
statistically.

The I.Q. scale is so powerful because a small difference
in problem-solving ability, amounting, say, to ten I.Q.
points or a year or so in mental age, makes a big difference
— an "order-of-magnitude difference" — in the difficulty of
problems that can be solved. I have on my desk an amusing pocket guide to the restaurants of New York, published
for engineers, which lists, among other things, the estimated
I.Q. of the waiters in each restaurant. And it is startling
to realize, as you do when you use this guide, how much

more pleasure there is in eating where the waitress has a normal I.Q. of 100, alert and competent, than where the service is at the 90 or 80 level, subnormal, with inattentive service and misunderstood orders.

And the I.Q. scale covers a vast range of these order-of-magnitude differences. An adult chimpanzee can solve mechanical problems about as well as a six-year-old child and might be assigned an I.Q. of around 40 if he were an adult human being. A moron would be around 70, an average person 100, a Ph.D. student 140, and Pasteur and Einstein 180 or over.

The importance of ten-point differences is just as striking at the 140 level or the 180 level as it is at the 100 level. The Ph.D. student can see order-of-magnitude differences in his professors that the man in the street might not see at all or might interpret backwards. Science is not so different from rock-climbing, which I once took some lessons in. It was only after the class had learned to claw their way up an easy fourth-degree slope that they began to appreciate the real risks and the beautiful performance of the men on the sixth-degree overhang up above.

The first hard fact for society about such a scale as the I.Q. scale is that, just as in mountain-climbing, there are certain problems that cannot be solved except by men of the very greatest abilities. To prove the germ theory of disease or to make the first atomic pile, you need to have a 180 mind around. This is equally true in organic chemistry, in philosophy; also in statecraft; probably in music and poetry; and perhaps in art, as the example of Leonardo suggests. It does no good to assemble dozens of 170's or hundreds of 160's for such problems, except on the chance that there may be a 180 hidden among them. Seventeen

Johnsons and Popes will not make a Shakespeare. On any problems that demand analytical thought and creation, men who work closely together are sensitive to differences of three or four points in each other's abilities. On the great problems, a difference of 10 points in some ability that is very much like I.Q. is what makes the final difference between achieving a solution and achieving a muddle.

I think the Sherlock Holmes stories are one of the best descriptions in print of these differences in analytical skill at the higher levels. Sherlock is about a 170, while the clumsy detective Lestrade is about a 140. (Sherlock's brother Mycroft, who can solve mysteries just by sitting and thinking about them, is evidently a 180.) Lestrade's mistakes are the 140 mistakes — premature generalization, failure to understand the nature of proof or what a crucial experiment is.   He does have an inquiring mind, and energy; what he lacks is rigor of analysis. Lestrade has the motivation, but only Holmes has the insight to find the hidden little key that unlocks the door; and the insight can hardly be explained or communicated until after the proof is in.

One of the troubles in science is that there are twenty Lestrades messing up the footprints and confusing the evidence for every Holmes who goes back to fundamentals and straightens it out. In nuclear physics it has recently turned out that for ten years, the best experiments on beta-decay have been either wrong or misleading. Not really Lestrade results; just the elusiveness of the wily Moriarty again; and they are on the track once more. But this field is lucky. Most fields have nothing but Lestrade results for decades at a time.

There is an apocryphal story that physicists tell about

the late John von Neumann — probably a 180 — that shows the difference they feel between such really high-speed minds and those of ordinary brilliance. It seems that a psychologist brought von Neumann the following problem. Two bicyclists are ten miles apart, each cycling toward the other at ten miles per hour. A fly starts from one cyclist's nose, flies off at twenty miles per hour to the other cyclist, then back to the first, and so on, back and forth, until the cyclists meet. How far does the fly fly?

The psychologist, according to this story, was giving this problem to various physicists and mathematicians and trying to distinguish the one type of mind from the other by the kind of solutions they gave. The mathematicians were supposed to take about one minute (!) to solve it, because they would figure out how far the fly went on each leg of the zigzag and then sum up this (infinite) series of legs to give the total distance flown. The physicists, however, were supposed to solve it much faster, in about fifteen seconds; because they would figure immediately that the cyclists would meet in half an hour, and in that time the fly at his speed would have flown just ten miles.

But when the problem was put to von Neumann, he solved it in ten seconds! The psychologist said, "How is this? You're supposed to be primarily a mathematician, not a physicist! You should have summed the series and taken one minute, instead of using velocities and taking fifteen seconds."

Von Neumann replied, "But I did sum the series!"

Psychologists have indeed been studying the mental processes of physical scientists lately, and with similarly baffling results. One psychologist reported seriously that half the physicists were anti-social because they didn't answer his letters, and that the other half were neurotic because they visualized Rorschach patterns in three dimensions! For this kind of Lestrade to be let loose on such a study is exactly as pathetic as for a subnormal waitress in the 90 range to try to measure the intellectual differences in college students.

Unfortunately few of us are big enough or matter-of-fact enough not to be offended when a smart man shows that he knows he is smart. I saw one nuclear physicist — a 180 analytically but perhaps something less in his social skills — antagonize a whole audience during a debate at a meeting, when he said bluntly, "I do not quarrel with third-rate scientists. I quarrel with first-rate scientists." One man said afterwards, "What does he expect me to do — shoot myself?"

He was emotionally involved because he still thought of himself as competing. Twenty points lower down the I.Q. scale and he would merely have been amused. Only a competing violinist could be envious of Heifetz. Only a competing basketball team would resent the height of the Harlem Globetrotters or expect them to be modest about it. When the intellectual levels are far enough apart, they can work at different kinds of problems, can serve each other and be served, appreciate and admire each other, without contempt or resentment. It takes all of our levels of ability to keep a civilization functioning. But our mutual dependence should not blind us to the fact of mutual difference.

The difference in problem-solving ability between the mind of the good Pasteur and the lowest mind that can still be called human is as great as the difference between an average man and a chimpanzee.

INTELLECTUAL SCARCITIES

The second hard fact is that there are not very many of these brilliant men at the top of the I.Q. scale. At the 190 level, which might describe Archimedes, Newton, and Gauss, we have been seeing about one every five hundred years. The recent increases in population and in the percentage of people who go into analytical fields will make the rate faster. (Ninety per cent of all the scientists who ever lived are living today.) At the 180 level there might be a dozen living Americans. This is the level, say, of Darwin, Freud, Shaw, Bertrand Russell, Percy Bridgman, Linus Pauling. Name your own. By the time we get down to 170, there are some three hundred in the U.S.; at 160, about five thousand; at 150, about one hundred thousand; at 140, about one million.

As soon as you say seriously that a man is one of the fifty or so brightest minds in the country — or one of any other number — you have placed him remarkably well on this scale. The smartest man in an average community of 1000, or the brightest pupil in an average high school of this size, will be up in the 140's, Ph.D. material. Half a dozen or so in such a school are the ones we depend upon to make our scientists, engineers and doctors.

Do many of these go unrecognized? It is true that some of the great ones have been slow in school. (Think how slow a human would seem at chimpanzee lessons.) Every teacher imagines that one of his daydreamers is simply stepping to the music of a different drummer. But most of those who make their mark show some sign early and are picked for success. Some studies indicate that in America at least half of the white Protestant boys capable of getting

Ph.D.'s in the physical sciences do get them. The 170's —
the one-in-a-million's — may get their Ph.D.'s as young as
twenty-two or twenty-three, some three years earlier than
the 140's, and they will have international reputations before they are thirty-five. There is no difficulty in spotting
them, and teachers and patrons rush in to help them along.

What have these statistics to do with society? I claim
that they show us a good deal about what we can expect of
Congressmen, schoolteachers and schoolchildren, college
students and many other groups. Obviously we can always
use more people at the top. The care with which we
identify them early and help them find the great teachers
they need and deserve is what governs our ability to win
Nobel prizes, to find cures for cancer and schizophrenia
and to make rockets and radar.

But what about the people below the top? For example,
the question is often raised whether Congress is really
stupid or only acts that way. The answer is that I.Q.
estimates from their educational records and occupations
show that as a group, Congressmen are pretty smart, mostly
in the 130's and above. This is the range where some psychologists say we find maximum leadership. Einstein is
supposed to have said that the trouble with chemists is that
chemistry is too hard for them. If our representatives collectively have trouble knowing what to do about national
and international problems, it is not because they are individually stupid, it is because these problems are almost im-
possibly hard for them or for anyone else. But as far as
brains are concerned, I doubt if we could get a better group
of several hundred men to represent us than those we have.

What about teachers? In our present educational setup
we need about one of them per thirty pupils, or one per

hundred of the whole population. This means some two million teachers. If we took every woman over 130 for this job, we would barely have this number. It is therefore one of the facts of life that teachers will generally have I.Q.'s in the 120 range. This means that most will be unable to graduate from very good colleges, and so the notoriously poor quality of teachers' colleges is almost a necessary evil. Leading citizens — in the 130 range themselves — will be contemptuous of such teachers, and bright children of thirteen or fourteen — the 130's and 140's — will already know more than most of their teachers. There is no help for it, except, first, to help the bright children get the very best teachers and the best outside help to enlarge their horizons. (If the professional people and intellectuals in every community each took on one protégé to enrich, it would be worth dozens of alarm meetings.)   And second, we need to use more and more educational television and movies so that the most brilliant of the teachers can reach thousands or millions of students at a time.

Or let us look instead at the children. The central problem of mass education is that half of the children are subnormal. By definition. This country has done one of the finest things in the world in extending education for the whole population to age eighteen; but we must not then expect them all to master the Latin and algebra and physics of the college-preparation courses that were suited to the top 5 per cent in the year 1900. In a democracy, with this great range of intellectual abilities, I think that equality of opportunity demands a separate kind of education for each level of ability. We would have to find some way to avoid the social stigma and bitterness that has plagued England's experiment in compulsory separation. Perhaps a more vol-

untary choice of the level of difficulty would be less conspicuous. Children, properly inspired, are eager to go as
far as they can; but they come to know their own limits,
too. I think that we must make a system where we can
challenge every student to his limit. But we must challenge
him in the range of his own abilities, not in the range of
abilities of a selected five per cent.

The difference in quality of American university students and British ones can also be understood immediately
from the I.Q. distributions. Until recently we have been
sending some 10 per cent of our boys and girls through
college — a fraction which reaches to the bottom of the
120's; while they have been sending less than one per cent
— or mostly 135's, if the selection is careful. Naturally
their education looks much better. But what we should
do is to compare their student performance only with the
top 10 per cent of our college group, that is, the A students.
The comparison is then not unfavorable at all. And in
graduate school, at the 140 level, where comparable per-
centages are tapped both here and there, our students are
universally acknowledged to be as good as or better than
their European counterparts, at least in the sciences. We
have been made to feel much too apologetic about our
magnificent experiments in mass higher education.

It is fascinating to examine group after group in this way,
ministers, doctors, civil servants, the entertainment industry, and many others, seeing the relevance of I.Q. distributions to our national problems. But I want to go on
here to discuss instead some interesting social phenomena
that today may be starting to produce dramatic changes in
these distributions.

COLONIES OF INTELLECTS

We may be beginning to get larger numbers of people at the top as a result of our strong intellectual selection in marriage.

It is all the result of coeducation. The smartest 10 per cent of our young people, the 120's and 130's, are now selected and thrown together in college at the most susceptible age for romance. About half the college men marry college women. Almost all the college women marry college men or, alas, remain unmarried.

This is preference, not just propinquity. I sometimes suspect that intelligence, smell, and politics are what really determine our choice of a mate. Dim-wits, garlic-eaters, and do-nothings must marry one another. It gives them the reassuring atmosphere of home. More seriously, I think that close friendships and free marriages do not often bridge an I.Q. gap of more than twenty points.

The important thing is that these college marriages produce bright children. It is not certain whether the intelligence of a child is more a matter of inheritance or of early stimulation, although some psychologists now suspect the latter. But whatever the explanation is, it looks today as if the children of the college marriages are clustering about the average of their parents' abilities, scattering above and below in much the same way that children of unselected parents scatter above and below the average of the whole population. If this proves to be so, it has the remarkable consequence that these marriages are now producing *five or ten times* the total number of 150's, for example, that we would get from perfectly random marriages in the normal population!

Even more spectacular children may be coming out of

the intellectual colonies like Oak Ridge or Los Alamos, where one man in six has a Ph.D.; or the faculty communities of the great universities, where all the men and many of the women have advanced degrees. Collectively these communities really form a small town of 20,000 people or so, with the Ph.D.'s moving around from one colony to another as frequently as DuPont branch managers. They all know each other, more or less, and large social circles of 130's and 140's spring up in such centers. When the children go to a common — or uncommon — school, whole classes of 130's and 140's may be seen, from kindergarten through high school.

In the general population with an average I.Q. of 100, only one person in 300 reaches the 140 level. But in communities with an average of 140, does one child in 300 reach 180? and one in 2000 reach 190? If this turns out to be so, we may not have to wait centuries for the next Newton; we may have a dozen Newtons within twenty years. The number of 180's getting out of college in the next few years may not be a mere dozen, but hundreds. It could be an explosion of genius such as the world has never seen.

I actually think I see some of these real geniuses sprouting around me today. A thirteen-year-old is studying atomic physics seriously, an eleven-year-old is taking college courses, an eight-year-old is doing graduate work in mathematics. Even in a university community they are frightening — and wonderful. How do we root them and shield them and yet challenge them and educate them for civic and world responsibility? That is the most important problem for their parents and perhaps also for the nation. If I am right about this crop, it is not far from the mark to speak of a new race of men.

Probably there are many people who feel uneasy about a

brilliant social group, just as there are people resentful of a brilliant individual. They may feel that it is somehow undemocratic to acknowledge the existence of such groups or to let them continue, or they may fear that such selective communities may begin to turn against the rest of society. I think any such fears are unjustified. The notion of malevolent genius is only found in fiction. It is almost a contradiction in terms. Nobel prize winners do not need to twist aside into Frankensteins. In real life, the really brilliant find the greatest exercise of their talents in serving society, not in trying to manipulate it for personal ambition. The intellectual communities I speak of have a record of civic and national responsibility both in war and peace that they can be proud of, and everyone can be proud of.

I do not think that there is any danger either that they will become somehow cut off from other people. The professors come into these communities from every background, and the scientists are, according to several studies, mostly middle-class boys from religious homes. They have not assembled in these groups to get away from mankind but to serve mankind by carrying on more efficiently their true business of enlarging knowledge.

In fact these groups are just one by-product of the general organization and maximization of intellectual development that is the central achievement of our century. All our other achievements really flow from this one. It is a kind of forced draft of the intellect. From grade school all through life, we stimulate individuals to excel, praise and reward them for it, and select the excellent for further challenges. We have organizations, industrial and governmental, to program invention and discovery, and to make them easier by breaking them down into consecutive steps that even little men can solve. Yet while the labor of creative work is being reduced, the talent to do it is continually stimulated by stirring the fire. The old molds of place, hierarchy and custom, that once permitted a man to stagnate after the age of thirty, are broken and broken again for our mobile scientists and managers. Intellectual communities spring up to house this constant flux of brilliance. These centers of research and learning interact more strongly than ever with every aspect of American life, from the Iowa farms to Cape Canaveral.

It all forms an intellectual furnace such as the world has never seen. Compared to this, mankind has never used its brains before. And I see new brains coming into service.

Thoreau says, almost as though he had looked at our statistics:

> The millions are awake enough for physical labor; but only one in a million is awake enough for effective intellectual exertion, only one in a hundred millions to a poetic or divine life. To be awake is to be alive. I have never yet met a man who was quite awake. How could I have looked him in the face?

He was talking about something more like renunciation and insight than science, but at this level of dedication the distinction almost disappears. He would have liked to meet the men awakening today.

MUSICIANS, POETS, MATHEMATICIANS

Once we have begun to appreciate the heights and depths of human intellectual achievement, we can go on to explore the diverse directions that achievement takes.

It seems to me that brilliance is naturally differentiated into two or three specialties. The classes that strike me most strongly as natural ones are the musicians, the poets, the mathematicians, and perhaps the painters. Two things are remarkable about these groups, first, that the brilliant youngsters may show their talent in these directions at a very early age, and second, that they may have a certain preference for marrying each other, not only according to their intelligence but according to their specialty. It may also be no accident that we are here brought back to exactly some of the fields that we found showed a masculine-feminine difference as well as an attraction for the high I.Q.'s.

Who can produce, before he is twenty-one, a masterwork that the whole world will appreciate for generations? Anne Frank, perhaps, but it is her circumstances and her innocence that touch us, I think, rather than a real genius. But there are many musicians who have produced great work early: Mozart, for example, composing at six; and Mozart and Bizet writing symphonies at seventeen that we still enjoy. There are poets also: Keats, Shelley. And mathematicians: Abel and Galois were dead almost before they were men.

Gauss was creating mathematics as a child. In the late 1930's, I remember Professor Laporte at the University of Michigan introducing the graduate students in physics every year to the method of summing an arithmetic series which Gauss discovered for himself. His introduction always started off in the same meticulous way, which we told each other about and came to listen for, like the first words of a fairy story: "The young Gauss, aged ten, had a very lazy teacher . . ."

It made a heart-sinking impression on the graduate students, aged twenty-three.

What is peculiar about these fields, music, poetry, and mathematics? We would not trust a judge or a doctor or a philosopher aged ten; or aged seventeen, either.

The answer is obvious: omission of the external world. These are the abstract fields, the fields of almost purely formal manipulation of symbols into patterns — musical symbols, verbal symbols, mathematical symbols. I think the visual symbols of painting and sculpture will have to be added to the list now. Under the apprentice system, Michelangelo, Raphael, and Van Dyck were all professionals before nineteen. With our recent understanding that there can be formal and abstract art as well as music, it may become possible for teen-agers even without apprenticeship to compose masterpieces of organization of space. (And why not restore apprenticeship, say for the brilliant ones? How many geniuses have we lost by making this kind of home or guild training rare or impossible in our present society?)

In fields requiring more human experience, beyond mere logic, success comes later and later. The Nobel prizes in physics and chemistry generally go to men in their thirties; but in medicine, to men in their forties; while in law and philosophy any similar achievements come first in the fifties and sixties. Even in the youthful formal fields, the works under twenty are not the greatest works of a creator's life. It takes more than just symbols, it takes external reference and understanding to move us deeply. But the symbolic manipulations are the sign of intellectual power.

If the youthful fields have this common aspect, does it mean that they represent just a single type of talent pushed into one direction or another by childhood accident?

Weierstrass said, "A mathematician who is not also something of a poet will never be a complete mathematician." Should this be taken literally? I think probably not. I suspect that the frequent association of physical, mathematical, and musical interests in the same man as exemplified by Einstein, was a cultural accident of the central Europe of a generation ago. Today the correlation has broken down. Young scientists today are mountain climbers rather than violinists and are more familiar with pitons than with pizzicato.

The second peculiarity of these natural fields of brilliance is that of inbreeding. It is most obvious in the musicians. America is now said to be the most musical nation in the world, with hundreds of symphony orchestras, more chamber music, a larger total attendance at concerts, and so on, than any other country. Adding up all the serious musicians in this crowd, say the ones who practice once a day or join a group to play or sing once a week, we may have 5 or 10 per cent of the adult population. But one of the interesting and important things about them is that they marry each other. They meet over the piano. They want music in the home. They go in clusters to Interlochen or Aspen or the Berkshire Festival, romance no objection, to form musical colonies more single-minded, even if shorter lived, than the intellectual university colonies I spoke of earlier. I have not been able to find any statistics on this subject, but my guess is that well over half the time those who are seriously musical marry others in the clan; so that they have an inbreeding at least as strong as the intellectual inbreeding in the coeducational colleges.

Why is this more significant than that people who like dancing or bowling should marry one another? or office employees? As of course they do, in much the same selective way. It is more significant because of the evidence we have seen that the musical mind may be a special type of mind. Aside from the question discussed earlier of masculine dominance in musical creation, the musical mind may be — may be, I emphasize — another genetic trait that only pops up in a few per cent of the population, like red hair. If it is, inbreeding among musicians could produce a group of people less and less like the nonmusical, as inbreeding is said to have produced in Scotland and Ireland whole villages of redheaded people.

Much the same is true, though to a smaller degree, among poets and writers. They have their classes and conferences, too, where the sexes meet in an atmosphere of respect and sympathy. The English instructor doesn't marry the beautiful nurse; he marries the lit major who knows what he is talking about. I cannot say whether the same is true of mathematicians; they are so few in number, and the girl mathematicians are much fewer still. But in physics, the next field over, up to half of the girl graduate students marry physical scientists. (These, and the unmarried, are the only ones who continue professionally; presumably for the others, who make the "mistake" of marrying outside the field, the scientific habits and hours of work must give way to the husband's concept of home life.) Do artists and architects breed true? No one has suggested it; but there are artists' colonies.

I am fascinated by these trends but I am not sure what to make of them. It would be queer if we really could inherit a talent for manipulating particular kinds of symbols, for the symbols seem to me to be somewhat accidental historical creations of the human race, not biologically fundamental. Our verbal and musical symbols scarcely represent the whole field of possible sounds; painting, sculpture and architecture scarcely scratch the surface of the organization of visual space; and I am not sure that mathematical symbols represent all the forms of biological logic. What new kinds of symbols are we preparing to manipulate, color organs, Labanotation for the ballet, or a dozen others, calling for new talents and developing new types of youthful genius?

But whether brilliance in these arts will be inherited or only acquired by the children, the colonies and concentrations of specialists may be taking the human race branching into new directions. As geographical isolation breaks down, the great historical races of man, with their so-obvious external animal differences of noses and skin, are amalgamating on a hundred fronts. The internal differences, however, the differences of sheer intellect and of various kinds of abstract creativity, may be diverging into new races of mind, all Newtons, Beethovens, and Michelangelos, as far removed from what we have called normal as what we have called normal is removed from the gorilla.

What symphonies they will compose! What laws they will discover! What centuries lie ahead!

7. THE ART OF
CREATIVE THINKING

THE FACTORS in creative intellectual work have been discussed for thousands of years. Everyone is interested in the question whether, by taking thought, he can add some cubits unto his intellectual stature. It does not seem so impossible now as it once did. Whole populations now increase in physical height — certainly a less variable characteristic than the intellectual powers — by one or two inches in every generation, presumably as a result of better nutrition and control of disease; and no one can say how far up we may shoot.

Perhaps we have also been intellectual dwarfs deprived of important growth factors until now. Such factors as personal attention are said to raise the I.Q.'s of orphans, and tutoring is believed to raise those of ten-year-olds in England about to take their pre-university examinations. The average American is said to be about ten points higher on the old intelligence tests than a generation ago. Small fry now know the days of the week and the months of the year almost a year younger than they did then. This is probably not due to any increase in mental agility, but just to the enrichment of the children's culture, from the child-oriented parents to the TV set. Yet it represents a measurable increase in our collective mental altitude.

This all suggests that a single individual, even an adult, might also be able to make considerable increases in his own intellectual level if he could find ways to give himself similar challenges and enrichment. This conclusion seems to be borne out by an examination of the factors — particularly the motivational ones — in intellectual and creative work, and an examination of the working habits of the most prolific men. Most of the examples I will give are taken from the sciences, but mental activity in other fields, even in the smaller arenas of the farm, the household or the office, must have similar factors and similar problems of motivation and challenge.

Direct self-improvement by lifting one's own mental bootstraps, with numbered instructions on how to do it, is advocated in numerous popular self-improvement guides. Some people probably have to take these uplifting prescriptions periodically, like cathartics, so as to feel purposeful again. After some initial skepticism, I now find myself agreeing with the claims of these guides that most of us use only a fraction of our possible creative powers. I agree with their point that a real creative intention is necessary for success; but I think it is not by direct self-exhortation and resolution that we can increase our powers but by numerous indirect rewards, like the little devices used by prolific men, devices whose steady presence makes a person enjoy thinking consecutively and coherently about his major concerns. Direct control of thinking is a contradiction in terms. A person who is trying to focus on Point Six is as much distracted from real thinking as another man would be by a pair of pretty ankles, and much less naturally.

A period of searching self-examination seems to have been necessary for many great men, such as William James and Yehudi Menuhin, before they could release at last the creative power and scope of a deeply satisfied personality in harmony with itself. To develop the very greatest powers, the forty days in the wilderness may be a creative necessity. But I think we need not get into such deep questions of personal integration here. Most of us would be more harmed than helped by such self-probing, like the centipede who tried to remember which leg moved after which and lay distracted in the ditch, considering how to run. It is probably best for a brilliant youngster to practice his creative powers for some years and get firmly in the habit of them before he begins to question them too much.

The aim here is simply to show as objectively as possible that creative success, or problem-solving in the widest sense of the term, can be factored into three or four basic elements about as cleanly as, say, mountain-climbing, which is a close physical analogue of the intellectual process. We can identify what the chemist might call the "rate-determining steps" in the analytical process. And the successive steps can be made easy and enjoyable and habitual by perfectly straightforward biological feedbacks and indirect motivational devices.

Much of what I have to say about mental work will be simply what every thinking man formulates for himself in one language or another — if he stops and thinks! But some of the working methods to which I want to call attention seem to have an effectiveness which has been little appreciated, at least by scientists. The indications here are that if scientists and psychologists applied to the intensifying of creative work what we now know about feedback and amplification effects, still better methods might be found; and the wider use of such work schemes might lead to a tremendous increase of powers for the whole intellectual community, a considerable advantage to any group or nation that first discovered how to bring it about.

Let us look at the framework of the intellectual problem-solving processes, the operational factors that go into a successful result. Several of the factors in intellectual accomplishment show up clearly when we consider the differences in different children. We suspect first that there is a genetic factor. In the cradle, one infant is far more alert and inquisitive than another. It also seems to be pretty well established that genius does tend to run in families, in spite of counter examples such as the undistinguished parentage of Leonardo, Newton, and Shakespeare.

But the development of civilized intellectual powers requires two more things. First, that the child be presented with civilized problems; and second, that he be given civilized symbolic apparatus or so-called conventional signs to handle these problems. We all know the value of symbols in increasing mental clarity and power. Musical prodigies come from musical homes where they have learned the notes. A wild mathematical genius would have to spend a lifetime creating his own number system if he had been taught no words for the numbers beyond two. A Basuto child is handicapped in learning chemistry if he has no reading or writing or arithmetic until his teens. This is what public education is for, to create a population that can communicate and solve problems that most of us would never solve by the capricious development of our innate talents. What unguessed kinds of symbolic apparatus still lie beyond us, that might be taking our children just as much farther again?

In addition, as some psychologists now emphasize, early environmental stimulation — the presentation of challenging problems — may be a major factor in developing a child's intelligence. Brilliance in school frequently follows upon early enrichment in the home. It may be that many of our children — not all, but the brightest — are kept as much below their potentialities as the Basuto child by having no reading or writing or arithmetic until they are six. What an average child can do at six, a 180 I.Q. can do at three. Or is it that the one who does it at three is thereby lifted closer to the 180 I.Q.? No one knows. But there seems to be a strong possibility that we might greatly increase the numbers of our brilliant men if more mothers would start step-by-step educational stimulation and challenge at the cradle or just beyond.

I think the same factors — native ability, challenge and symbolic apparatus — are still important in adults, but adults have learned to ignore most challenges, and their success in responding to a problem depends on the attention and time they give to it. Another factor also enters their problems, namely, complexity; and success often depends on the skill with which a complex problem can be broken up. We are thus led to the following components in adult intellectual achievement:

In Problem-Solving	*In Mountain-Climbing*
1. Intellectual or creative ability	Physique and skill
2. Time spent per day in formal application	Time spent climbing
3. Symbolic apparatus	Feet, ropes, ladders, cable cars
4. Skill of breakdown of problem into short sure steps	Analysis of feasible paths to the top. Rules for steps

Opposite each intellectual factor I have indicated its equivalent in physical problem-solving such as mountain-climbing. The parallel with this more familiar and more objective discipline reassures us that we are distinguishing the factors correctly and have not omitted any. It may help to prevent such errors as the all too common one of confusing intellectual ability with intellectual level.

INTELLECTUAL ABILITY

Most of us will believe that there is some basic intellectual ability, some moment-by-moment power of the reasoning or creative machine, that is fundamental to adult intellectual success. Our discussion of it can be brief, since any such factor cannot be much subject to conscious control. Possibly we are born with minds destined to have a certain speed of operation and a certain skill in analogy and extrapolation at a certain age. Possibly we improve these qualities somewhat with practice. But at eight o'clock on Thursday morning I cannot, by taking thought, add one cubit to my stature or one kilowatt to the mental horsepower with which I do my work that day.

Nevertheless the subject should not be dropped without mentioning the physiological effects which give us an indirect control, and which people should take far more account of in intellectual activity than they do. Drugs, for example, can affect an intellectual race as well as a horse race. Whether they have a beneficial effect on the creative abilities that is not outweighed by their side effects is a question still debated with more heat than information and one that each person must decide for himself. Artists, writers, and some statesmen aid their mental powers with alcohol, students and truckdrivers use benzedrine, all Americans use caffeine, and more and more creative people are using the milder modern tranquilizers and energizers.

Some achieve remarkable results by alternating the stages of uninhibited creation, properly titrated with stages of sober critical judgment to correct the excesses. Certain trace necessities such as Vitamin A, Vitamin C, and nicotinic acid are also said to put the machinery into high gear and are easy enough for anyone to try without misgivings. Many of the differences in personal force and mental quickness between different people may be due to natural biochemical differences in the level of such trace materials.

Mental abilities also change, like athletic abilities, with sleep and diet and time of day, differently for each person. Probably these changes are related to the brain's well-known sensitivity to oxygen, carbon dioxide, and blood sugar levels. Is this why several prominent mathematical physicists have been compulsive eaters of sweets? The old scholarly phrases, the odor of the lamp, the midnight oil, the smoke-filled study — are they intellectual chemistry as well as metaphor? I mention such speculations here only to suggest how much we have yet to learn about the biochemical conditions for intellectual work. A little money spent on intelligent research on these questions — perhaps using matched chess players as subjects — might pay off handsomely. I see no reason to doubt that the right vitamins and hormones and other drugs will eventually be found to make at least as much difference to our peak intellectual health and performance as they do to our peak physical health and performance.

THE MEASURE OF ANALYTICAL THOUGHT

The other three factors in intellectual achievement are subject to more conscious control. Consider factor two. How much time did you spend today in formal application of your intellectual powers, or more precisely, in analytical thought? Don't try to get out of it by asking me to define analytical, or by saying that every thought is analytical. You know, and I know, the difference between reading the paper or cleaning house or sitting in a discussion or writing letters or even giving lectures, and *thinking*. Analytical thinking is Sherlock Holmes thinking, figuring out from small clues the height of the criminal and whether he was left-handed. Have you made any large inference today from close observation? It does not require civilization. The successful tracker or hunter must think like this. It does not require mathematics. It can be found in the better organization of housekeeping, or in the artist's consideration of another way to represent a shadow. Any consecutive thought about what you do, why you do it that way, what would happen if you did it slightly differently, is analytical reasoning.

I would like to suggest the convenience of having a rough unit of analytical reasoning so that we can talk more or less quantitatively about how much thinking is involved in this job or that. I think a good unit would be the amount of reasoning involved in a forty-move game of chess or a hard end-game problem, or a fairly hard (for you) crossword puzzle; that is, half an hour to an hour of problem-solving. This might be called "one gamesworth" of reasoning, to give it an obvious name. It is a useful unit because we are all acquainted with such problems and have a feeling for their difficulty — easily distinguished from ten-minute problems on the one hand and from three-hour problems on the other. I also think the sequence of mental operations is fairly typical of formal thinking on complex problems, a mixture of memory, rules of procedure, deductions, analogies, inductions, evaluations and insight, all leading to an elegant and novel solution with the loose ends tied up. Also we shall see that it is a natural unit, measuring roughly the amount of reasoning most of us can do at one sitting.

Many of us do crossword puzzles every day, but I think that few do a gamesworth of serious reasoning every day. Sherlock Holmes lived for nothing else, but most people, even creative artists and scientists, are creatures of habit and only *think* occasionally. This is unfortunate. Our highest powers lie unfocused. Count that day lost whose low descending sun sees from thy mind no gamesworth of reasoning done. "There are some problems you cannot solve in a million years unless you think about them for five minutes," to quote a famous saying of the physicist M. L. Goldberger. If, one day, a hundred million adult Americans all gave one gamesworth of thought to their work, the world would tremble and mankind would never be the same again.

There is nothing impossible about applying the mind in a more or less concentrated way for a good part of every day, if you set up the conditions for it; and this is the straightforward explanation given by many prominent men for their achievements. In *Men of Mathematics*, E. T. Bell quotes Gauss: "If others would but reflect on mathematical truths as deeply and continuously as I have, they would make my discoveries." And when Newton was "asked how he had made discoveries in astronomy surpassing those of all his predecessors, Newton replied, 'By always thinking about them.'"

Sir William Osler emphasized the importance of single-minded concentration by saying: "There are two kinds of people, skylarks, who work in the morning, and nightingales, who work late at night. And there are two rules for success in medical research: Don't get married until you are thirty-five; and be born a nightingale."

In short, avoid the two worst interruptions, Families and Other People. Every field has its folklore about the success of the nightingales. Maybe they are born so, maybe not. But much of their secret must be that they are ready to do analytical reasoning at a time of minimum external distraction, while the more conventional skylarks are trying to think at a time of maximum distraction. The seduction of the mind to think obeys the old formula for other types of seduction: Find the place and the time, and the rest will take care of itself.

Actually I believe that the time need not be very long, that no one really spends a whole working day every day in the kind of intense analysis I am talking about. In the purest mathematics there is much routine operation to be carried out; and I suspect that the chess wizard who plays all day long is dealing most of the time with familiar situations.

Probably the brain, like the rest of our physiology, is designed for maximum power output in short bursts only. The tiger sprints away, but he tires quickly and the trained horse can easily run him down. We eat for an hour, hear a lecture or a play or a concert for no more than an hour or two or three. Patience and interest flag. In some sense the brain is indeed tired. I suggest that in concentrated analytical thought, one or two gamesworth every day would be about the maximum for most of us. This much actual thought — a couple of crossword puzzles' worth — is not so distressing to contemplate, is it? This principle is often neglected in the long hours and numerous courses of our schools.

We can confirm this rough upper limit by looking at the output of the most prolific men. Jefferson's writings fill fifty volumes, say one per adult year. Benjamin Franklin, that "printer, statesman, writer, seller of books, philosopher, civic leader, linguist, inventor (of bifocal spectacles, a harmonica, a stove, among other things), scientific experimenter, superb autobiographer, tireless correspondent and postal-system innovator," had a similar output. At their peak, Shakespeare and Shaw produced two or more plays per year. Dickens and Scott, one or two novels per year. John Dickson Carr and Simenon, today's high-speed writers of detective novels, turn out four to ten per year. Mozart produced an opus every week or two. Euler produced over a thousand pages per year, largely algorithms; his manuscripts fill a museum room and have scarcely begun to be examined. Kelvin turned out six hundred scientific papers, roughly one a month. Today the astronomers, with their numerous stars, and the chemists, with their numerous molecules — and their numerous graduate student assistants — occasionally match this rate.

For this kind of literary and semi-literary activity, the maximum rates then seem to be in the range of two hundred to one thousand pages per year, averaging steadily about one page per day, within a small factor. Much of each page is of course grammar rather than ideas, and I would guess that this output represents of the order of one or two gamesworth of chesslike reasoning per day, say thirty to one hundred moves. A man might generate ten times as much volume with a dictating machine but scarcely ten times as much reasoning. Averaged over the years, a tightly written page is then not far from a day's work or a natural unit of reasoning, in music or mathematics or letters. A tightly written paper or opus or chapter is evidently something like a larger natural unit of organization, which might be generated in one to four weeks of consideration and absorbed in an hour. Many of the productions of the most prolific men bear a light spontaneous stamp, and one suspects that men famous for a smaller number of works have produced at comparable rates but have revised more extensively and have been more critical about what they kept. Franklin Roosevelt is supposed to have said of Churchill that he had a hundred ideas a day, four of them good; this was enough to make the difference from an ordinary man.

Some men, literary and otherwise, may try to justify a small output on the grounds of selectivity. Stephen Spender carries things to their logical conclusion when he says, "It does not matter whether genius devotes a lifetime to producing a small result if that result be immortal."

This is a stern doctrine. Evidently poets do not have to eat, as physicists do. It also provokes the observation that the actual act of creation of the small result — immortal or otherwise — does not take a lifetime at all, but frequently only a few hours, when the moment is ripe. Schubert's best songs were written in a day, Frost's best poem in an hour, the Schrödinger equation in a weekend, and the theory of evolution by Wallace in a couple of days; Darwin's life of work was but the massive buttressing of the brief immortal idea. Who knows what immortal little result you are but two hours away from: Have you done — or revised — your page of thought today?

Thought about what?, you may say. You are not a

Schubert or a Schrödinger. Thought cannot exist in a vacuum; it must have something to think about. Quite true. Lofty subjects or simple ones. Each person must start with his own problems; if nothing else, the funny or surprising regularities of the day that are the staples of chat. But I believe that the process, and the advantage, of applying one's mind more connectedly and formally is much the same whether the thinking is applied to children's tantrums or to rocketry. Write them down explicitly, the causes and effects, the interactions and implications, what would happen if you changed this or that. Could mail delivery be made more efficient here? Other communications channels? What are the pros and cons of setting up an operations research group? Can I think of a definitive experiment to check the causal chain in these correlations? Is Billy's upset due to hunger or an aggressive playmate? Where could a few of us spend $50 to beautify this street most strikingly?

Naturally thoughts are more consequential if they are on important subjects, and on subjects you know something about; and it is better if you go on with the same subject and make a record of your thoughts day after day, so that they build up into something. But trivial ideas are fun, too — the guerrilla operations of the mind — where you get some quick objective satisfying little result and success is easy to see. Whether a serious subject or a trivial one, related to your work or outside it, give it a gamesworth of thought — all the thought it needs for an important little result — and then think how you should act on the result.

From the figures on the prolific workers and from the immortal instances, I conclude that a page or a gamesworth or two of thought every day is about the maximum; and yet that this amount is possible for everyone and even easy. We all confess it, in our enjoyment of the daily crossword puzzle. Real thinking is brief and it is fun. It has nothing to do with being a grind or a worrier or a show-off or an intense young man. But to apply this short amount of thought to our own problems and then to act on it is so rare that the man who begins to do it systematically may soon distance competitors he has barely kept up with before. Feel no inferiority. The book you write in is your own and no one is inferior there. The daily intellectual tortoise can pass many a high-speed brain that only operates when fancy strikes.

The effort itself changes a person's outlook for the better. A gamesworth of thought takes so little time that a man who has done his hour of reasoning and has had even one idea — even a small one and still buried in the notebook — feels a sense of success and freedom for the rest of the day, or night. This alters his whole attitude toward other more routine chores and toward the practical work of translating his idea into output. He has already done his real work for the day, and the lesser problems then fall into easy perspective. First things first, and the rest will be added unto you.

This pleasure and confidence is seductive, and makes it easy to go on with such a program — one of the motivational feedbacks. I think this is one of the secrets of the habitually relaxed attitude that prolific minds so often show. The brilliant British physicists and chemists with their short hours and long teas do not have to sweat and strive, because they have learned how to think formally. Somerset Maugham took the view that if he could not become rich and famous by writing until noon, he could not do it by writing all day either.

SYMBOLIC APPARATUS

The third component of intellectual prowess is the use of the best available equipment. It is the nylon tents and oxygen tanks, and the easy donkey train as far as possible, that make the difference in climbing Everest. A man should lose no opportunity to upgrade his intellectual manipulative equipment; that is, the symbolic apparatus with which he does his mental operations.

The bricklayer, with his stretched string and try-square and clumsy bricks, no matter how economical and elegant his performance of the job, is climbing on foot while the manufacturer of prefabricated panels passes him by. Maxwell's work in electricity was able to remake communications and the world because he bridged chasms with his differential equations that could never have been crossed at all by the methods, say, of Galileo's geometry. The Bushman boy may spend two gamesworth of analytical reasoning and subtle skill to track down some animal. But after he is through, he has killed one animal. The Western boy who does the same amount of mental work on the mathematical and verbal symbols of his geometry or civics lesson in high school has gone up with a cable car to conquer heights more valuable to the human race in the long run than many animals. (He might do better if he could be given the corresponding thrill of accomplishment more frequently, too.)

We have no general index for the power of our symbolic apparatus. It might be helpful if we did, but I have been unable to think of any that satisfy me even qualitatively. It would be helpful to every research director and every company to be able to estimate more accurately the power of the methods that different men are using. Sometimes the symbols of one culture can be compared with those of another by comparing the power of the weapons — on a suitable logarithmic scale — that each can produce. The Toledo blade represented an empirical metallurgy manipulating symbols with more powerful implications than the technology of chipped flint arrowheads.

The power sequence of mathematical symbols is usually clear. It goes up with speed of remembrance, simplicity of rules, and breadth of application. The Romans, for example, were held back by their clumsy number system. A child today goes directly from finger-counting to Arabic notation. Before he is nine, he may be doing arithmetic that would have taxed Cicero severely. Having seen British children learning multiplication and division, I estimate that the American child is saved six months of schooling by our decimal coinage and would be saved at least six months more by the adoption of the metric system of weights and measures. When these little differences are multiplied by millions of artisans and statesmen, it makes a terrific difference to the power of the whole culture.

Today, some high school mathematics courses include the study of sets, groups, and fields, notions unknown in American education a generation ago. The speed of education of children depends only on our symbolic inventiveness. In thirty years, or a hundred, the nine-year-olds may be using symbols as far beyond ours as ours are beyond the Romans. I can easily imagine a time in ten or twenty years when transistorized desk computers are cheaper than math texts, and when students from ten to fifteen years old will spend on Boolean algebra and the logic and programming of these machines the time they now spend repetitiously and inefficiently in the complexities of long division and solution of quadratic equations. The new subjects would be not only easier but far more powerful symbolically and far more relevant to the work of the world.

Likewise in adult operations, mathematical or not, a man is badly handicapped if his implications are limited. We must understand instances before we can understand principles, but it is wasteful to use our problem-solving mind to multiply instances indefinitely. To use finger-counting when you might be using computing machines, to debate one employee's suggestion when you should be considering whole schemes of optimization, to plan market tactics without using game theory, is operating at too low a symbolic level. It is like trying to fight a naval battle with rowboats.

In scientific work, the crucial experiment in a given field is at a different symbolic level in its implications from the noncrucial experiment, or the experiment that just uses the apparatus on hand. Pasteur's disproof of spontaneous generation was a crucial experiment. Its implication was the restructuring of a whole area of thought. Some fields are filled with men who do little but amass facts. Obviously this is necessary in the first survey studies, but it often comes to be an end in itself. One physical chemist, now in biology, says he is beginning to think we ought to pass a law against any scientist knowing more facts than he can account for. The fields of molecular biology and of nuclear physics have been so exciting in the last ten years because they are full of analytical young men who are not merely trying to measure something but to prove something, with maximum implication.

Likewise, once the experiment is chosen, the crucial points in its success — the keys to getting it to work — are at a different symbolic level from other aspects of the manipulations. When Pauling was asked why he looked first at such a complex molecule as hemoglobin in searching for genetic effects on protein chemistry, he replied that this substance could be obtained in quantity and purified and characterized more exactly than many apparently simpler molecules. It is operational simplicity, not paper simplicity, that is the crucial point for success. The difference in the great men, the Faradays and the Pasteurs and the Emil Fischers, is this search for operational clarity — what I am calling symbolic power — which shows up, first, in their repeated accuracy in picking out the crucial experiments that prove something; and second, in their repeated *Sitzgefühl* (to use a chess term) for the crucial points, the species to use, the gimmicks, the control of side effects, that will make the experiment work most conclusively. It would seem that almost anyone could learn to look for this operational clarity, but there are few teachers, even, who understand it.

When speaking in this general way of symbolic power, I have been thinking of a symbol as an X in a statement of the form "X implies . . ." where X might be a mathematical symbol, or a field of mathematics, or a generalization, or a manipulation or an experiment. Although my meaning is general, I think it is not ambiguous. But let me rail against those pseudo scientists who do not merely amass facts as ends in themselves, but invent pseudo-physical symbols as ends in themselves, I-percentages and W-factors and so on, apparently supposing that their non-mathematical disciplines will acquire power by giving every ambiguous notion a Roman letter. Probably something with boiling oil in it is the only cure for this. A written symbol must have a well-defined operational and manipulative meaning. The introduction of supposed symbols that have none is a scientific lie and can lead a whole generation astray.

Different symbols differ by so many orders of magnitude in their symbolic power — whether we can measure this quantitatively or not — that the man who uses powerful symbols can frequently get all the social reward he wants by an occasional bright idea and may not need to work very hard. From the company's point of view, ten minutes of thought on a problem by, let us say, Langmuir might be more valuable than eight hours or eight weeks of work by someone else. (Yes, a "consultant-fee index" to symbolic power might be possible.) The full-time employees who watch jealously the highly paid consultant flitting from here to there often realize neither how much more time he spends in formal thinking than they do nor how much more powerful his symbolic manipulations are.

Several years ago, the psychologist Roy John devised a machine that follows the reasoning of a person trying to solve a particular type of mechanical problem. He found that some persons would come back twenty times or more to pushing the same buttons in the same unsuccessful sequence, without either making a record of what they had done or stopping to think what the lack of success implied about the necessary next step. We are creatures of habit, and it is psychologically so much easier to repeat the same computations over and over "to be sure," or to debate and heckle and use gamesmanship when we should be writing down the alternatives for careful evaluation, that few of us use even one-tenth or one-hundredth of the symbolic apparatus we actually know how to manipulate, and even fewer go on to learn or invent still more effective short cuts.

If we did, whole industries would turn flip-flops.

STEPS TO THE TOP

The fourth component in adult creative success is the breaking up of big problems into a sequence of small steps. Recent experiments on learning seem to show that the elementary acts of learning do not require repetition, as had been supposed previously, but that we learn instantaneously a few small bits at each experience, a few more at the next, and so on. This is a new illustration of the general rule that mental jobs, like mechanical jobs, are done best if they are broken into small bits just the right size to manipulate easily.

In problem-solving, the bits must add up in sequence to form a path to the solution. Just as in climbing a mountain, you must think a little about the whole path in advance even though there are steps you cannot work out exactly until you get to them. You do not go up by the route you want to, but by the route you can, and often by the route you must. When you seem to be near the solution, you may still have to go back and start over a different way. Some problems can no more be solved by frontal assault than the east face of Long's Peak can be climbed straight up. Sometimes we may take an easy step, sometimes a hard step, sometimes tangential or away from the goal; but if we are to get there, every single step must be short and sure and must start from the step before.

In this sequence, both in individual problem-solving and collective problem-solving, special attention is being given today to separating clearly the stage of conjecture from the stage of criticism, so that the necessary creative conjecture will flow freely. Edward Teller has expounded the doctrine of "The Sixth Idea," saying that some problems can be solved only by taking five impossible ideas and then finding the sixth one that, combined with them, will make the whole scheme workable. In rough country, the wheel is obviously a useless invention and so is the road, until you put them together. The Wright brothers had to invent not only the airscrew and a kind of aileron, but also the wind tunnel to optimize them in. Such multiple requirements were an almost impossible block to primitive invention up to this century; but they need not be impossible, either for technical or social inventions, when we combine conjectures systematically before criticism.

Some recent books treat particularly cogently the tactics of research and the tactics of inductive problem-solving (as distinguished from the strategy, which can still be learned only from great teachers) and they give the conditional sequence of steps in considerable operational detail. One of these books is E. Bright Wilson, Jr.'s *Introduction to Scientific Research*. Others are G. Polya's primer *How to Solve It* and his two more advanced volumes *Induction and Analogy in Mathematics* and *Patterns of Plausible Inference*, which together he calls *Mathematics and Plausible Reasoning*. Wilson's whole point is that skill in research can be taught. Polya's point — by no means limited to mathematics! — is that skill in inductive inference can be taught, almost as well as the old Greek skill in deductive inference. I am fond of telling my students that *How to Solve It* will increase their scientific prowess by a factor of three; and that they should dip into Wilson every morning, as the devout of the last century dipped into the Bible, because on every page there is some important reminder for the day.

The problem of problem-solving has been the hardest

problem for us to solve. These and other recent books represent a closer analysis of this problem than we have had before. In science, as in mountain-climbing, we have been going up at haphazard and by luck, too dazzled by the great ones to follow the short sure steps of their footwork; but the procedure can be codified and learned so that anybody can scale heights that even the great ones would not have dared a short time ago. Heretofore, problem-solving has been too vague for exact criticism to show what step went wrong, or what kind of speed can be expected. I think when this kind of close analysis actually gets into common laboratory and industrial practice, reinforced by an immediate response of exact criticism and mutual inspiration, it will amount to a further explosion of genius. For illustration I would like to quote here some of Polya's list of questions — questions to ask oneself when stuck on a problem — but I will not, for fear of making what is simple and profound and should be instinctive appear to be merely trivial. It may not seem very profound to tell the beginner in mountain-climbing over and over again, Use your leg muscles instead of your arm muscles, Use your toes and not your knees; but these are the first principles — ones that the outsider might think either unnecessary or obvious — that have to be hammered into him before he can be either safe or skillful. It is good to have books now to help do this hammering for intellectual climbers.

8. THE MOTIVATION
OF CREATION

IN THE PRECEDING chapter we spoke of the symbolic apparatus connected with thought and of various rules for making short sure steps toward intellectual accomplishment. Now let us look at the motives which keep this machinery running energetically and their exemplification in the work methods of particular men.

Every prospective scientist or artist has some long-range and perhaps dim ambition that motivates him, perhaps growing out of some childhood admiration or some disturbance, as they tell us. But no one becomes a great writer just by telling himself and all his friends at the table over and over about his ambition. The big motive has to be supported by the immediate desire to write, after each breakfast, and a line-by-line preference and satisfaction in doing this rather than anything else hour after hour and day after day. Anything a person tries to do without having this instantaneous satisfaction most of the time will be done badly or not at all. Our educational failure to create an equation-by-equation and test-tube-by-test-tube excitement and satisfaction in the work is, I think, responsible for the loss of many prospective scientists and for the routinizing of many others.

Recent experiments on learning in dogs show that if a problem is set up so that the dog comes perceptibly closer to his reward immediately — that is, within a fraction of a second — after solving each step of a problem, the dog can learn tricks in sixty seconds that would require days or weeks to learn with the slower rewards of the usual teaching methods. Likewise the Link Trainer, which shows a pilot trainee his mistakes immediately, was found to be some five times faster for training airplane pilots than the old system using a human instructor. We can surely go much faster if we apply this principle to ourselves, in our schools and our work. The analytical part of the human mind is like a great baby that can be quickly coaxed along if a lollipop is in sight, but dawdles and gets sidetracked when it has to wait too long for approval and the reassurance that it is on the right track. It is no accident that many creative scientists as well as artists have been great vain egotists. Rutherford knew his worth and reveled in it. This is the external sign of a constant internal patting-on-the-back that gives the analytical brain confidence and keeps it working at maximum output.

For a creative individual (or a group) who wants to maximize his own output, the main problem as I see it is therefore to convert his long range ambition and motivation into increases in his little instantaneous rewards, fixing it so that these rewards will be greatest when his "creative efficiency" — his symbolic level and the shrewdness and accuracy of his steps forward — is highest. The mountain-climber is discouraged in a fog. He needs to have the feedback of seeing at every step whether he is on the best track and how much closer he is getting. In many, and perhaps in most, scientific or social problems, the instantaneous individual reward is what chemists would call the "rate-determining step" of the whole problem-solving process, and the speed and effectiveness of the response are what control the speed of solution. The path of a chemical reaction, the inevitable path, is down the sequence of the easiest or most attractive individual steps. If we want to solve any problem, we must make the path to a solution a sequence of individually desirable, and therefore inevitable, steps; so that the solution "goes by itself" without exhortation or flagellation; that is, down the local motivational hill. "Nature gives a prize to every single step in it," as Bagehot says in *Physics and Politics*.

There are prizes of various degrees of immediacy. Money is one of them. As soon as the nation of Israel paid the Yemenite children to go to school, so as to keep them from begging, they became so enthusiastic that many of their parents began to take adult education, too. When the University of Chicago experimented with a rule against outside income for the faculty, including royalties, the rate of book writing in the physical sciences dropped to less than one book per two hundred staff members per year; and the rule had to be changed. The royalties on scholarly books are nothing — perhaps thirty cents an hour; the feedback is everything. From Fresnel to Bethe, some of the greatest papers in physics were written for prizes. If some industrial concern would put up ten $1000 prizes for the best papers in the *Physical Review* each year, it would more than get its money back in the improved quality of the whole Journal.

Every creative man has his own more subtle devices to keep up his moment-by-moment satisfaction and drive. Herman Wouk is said to work in a bare study facing a clock that has a prominent second hand to remind him to keep going. Karl Marx said his mind would not think without a cigar. But there are three indirect devices that scientists and many others should adopt more generally because of their particular value in maintaining the instantaneous motivation to work with maximum shrewdness and at the highest symbolic level. These devices are: the notebook, the collaborator, and the audience. Absurdly obvious? Let me assure you that their motivational role in speeding up the "rate-determining step" is not appreciated by one scientist in twenty.

THE NOTEBOOK AS MOTIVATION

Artists have sketchbooks, writers have notebooks. I think it was Gladstone who told his son, Every day write in a book the balance of your ideas and the balance of your accounts. But scientists frequently have only some scribblings on a paper napkin. There is a story of a French *littérateur* conspicuously carrying a notebook who went up to Einstein at a cocktail party and said, "Dr. Einstein, where do you write down your ideas?" Einstein answered, "Nowhere. You see, I have one so rarely." This is probably the literal truth; he was manipulating symbols of such power that a few ideas in a lifetime were enough.

It is easy to extol and, among young theorists, fashionable to practice this relaxed superiority to record-keeping. The man who is searching for the superlative horse, in the sense of the Chinese fable, does not need to bother with such clerkish externalities. The greatest creations come to birth in a stable, radium in an old shed, atomic energy under the athletic stands, the equations of the world on the back of an envelope. The place is nothing, the intensity everything. It cannot wait. By the time the temple or the notebook has been prepared to channel it properly, the intensity has drifted elsewhere.

Nevertheless, more everyday research is done in properly equipped laboratories than on abandoned squash courts. And there have been men of the highest eminence in the sciences, men continuously productive for a lifetime, for whom a notebook was a necessity. Faraday's famous Diary is such a book. It illustrates several of the points here and is extremely instructive reading for any experimental man who seriously wants to maximize his output. Each day's entry in the Diary represents one or two gamesworth of analytical reasoning on the experiments which had just been completed. The usual industrial record book contains more writing but rarely so much thinking. Faraday writes down his conclusions, what is proved or disproved, and his hunches, and the outlines of what must be built or done next to clarify a point or to prove something more the next day. He then turns over the preparation of the new experiments to his assistant and goes home. (It is not clear when the assistant goes home.)

At the University of Chicago, the late Enrico Fermi's notebooks and work methods caused a good deal of rethinking among the physicists about the best way to organize problem-solving. In his theoretical years, for example, Fermi would work all day at the blackboard on whatever problem he had chosen, proceeding steadily from order-of-magnitude estimates of the major factors down to fine details. Every particularly pregnant result went into an indexed notebook. Other notebooks held data, and one was a "Memory" of useful numbers and equations. On most days apparently he would choose a new problem, and thus would give several gamesworth of thought to a series of problems in the course of a month. Some of the more interesting problems were worked through more extensively, and every year about four of these were finished into shape for publication, each a definitive paper representing many gamesworth of thought on a subject selected from all the others for its central importance. This is about the highest publication rate of any physicist today, but altogether represented the smaller fraction of his total studies.

Fermi was insatiably curious about everything. He once said that a scientist should spend two thirds of the work week on his own problems and one third absorbing other ideas to broaden his viewpoint and balance it. To do the latter, he thought the most efficient way was not to read technical papers but to go to seminars, where a number of people could hear an expert introduce a subject, give the salient points and answer criticism. He practiced this philosophy, read little, and attended more seminars and asked more questions than anyone else.

The result of these wide interests and concentrated work methods was omniscience in physics. It was hard to ask Fermi a question on any specialized topic to which he had not already devoted more gamesworth of thought than most experts, with the results all worked out in his notebooks. Taking care not to give offense, he would remember the crucial factors, even subtle ones that anyone else might overlook, he would know the problem's importance or lack of it, and frequently could give a fairly exact numerical answer.

One of our wits at Chicago says that the secret of success in theoretical physics is the ability to get rid of visitors and questioners. And that Physicist A does it by saying, You know so much more about that than I do; the questioner is then flattered and leaves. Physicist B says, But what about the X-effect? The questioner is mystified and leaves. But Fermi would do it by giving a numerical answer immediately, to three decimal places. This led to two subcases: (a) the questioner would go away and shoot himself, as being unworthy of being a physicist; or (b) he would take the answer and use it. In either case, he would leave.

Fermi's attitude in his work was that it was not worth doing anything unless you gave it your whole attention. It was better to miss even a good lecture than to go half alert or to pick up vague or sloppy information. It was better to ignore a problem than to fail to do it carefully and right. Once when he got up to correct a previous speaker, he said, more sharply than usual, "Whatever reputation I have comes from my competence at erasing a blackboard." It was no use to master something unless you made a permanent record of it in the notebook; and no use to make a record unless it was of something you understood.

Professor Chandrasekhar, the astrophysicist, who collaborated with Fermi on several problems, has said that the work methods of many theoretical physicists would be disastrous for anyone else to adopt; but that Fermi's methods can be adopted by anyone with profit. They may not make a smart man into a genius, but they will permit him to maximize the effectiveness of the talents he has. Every day a gamesworth of reasoning recorded about your work; and step by step you can build up your own kind of competence and omniscience in some area.

I know that in addition to formal reasoning there is other mental work to be done, by a scientist or anyone else — attentive survey observations, subliminal hints, the rejection of unsuitable directions, subconscious aesthetic criteria; and, in experimental science, the reasoning has to be turned into manipulations, hours of them per day. But the reasoning is what makes the manipulations minimal and elegant and what makes the difference between a crucial experiment and just another measurement. I think I am not undervaluing the average scientific paper in the Journals when I say that it represents only a gamesworth or two of overt reasoning (often distributed among several authors!). Even if we multiply this ten times over for the hidden effort, it would seem that most scientists are generating only one-tenth or less of the consecutive thought of a Faraday or a Fermi, not because of any lack of intellectual ability but because of something more like failure to focus; and that they might increase their scientific effectiveness many-fold with systematic daily aids to reasoning like the notebooks used by these men.

Putting the work into permanent bound notebooks is an essential element of this method. It has several motivational advantages. One of the young men who has been revolutionizing molecular biology always emphasizes to his colleagues "the necessity of thinking formally" instead of merely feeling or sliding into a conclusion. The notebook is a continual reminder of this necessity. For most of us, thought wanders without a visible line of work to refocus it from time to time. Also the most brilliant cocktail idea or the work on a piece of scratch paper is lost and scattered without a permanent record, and does not build into anything. The powers of civilized men are not due to an increase in our thinking ability but to a decrease in our loss rate.

The analytical mind needs to be exercised, and enjoys being exercised, like a horse or a dog, daily. The notebook is its exercise ground. The notebook is the immediate stimulus of the mind: Yum, says the mind, here's a neat problem, how do I get out the meat, how do I break it down? — Look what I wrote a week ago, that was a pretty good idea, I feel proud that's in the book — Oh, oh, two weeks ago, what a stupid conclusion, I've gone much farther than that now, I'll do it right. The notebook satisfies the mind as a record of achievement, as a pleasure to reread and criticize, and so at last a pleasure to anticipate adding to.

The notebook will force your reasoning to stay at the highest creative level you are capable of, because the critic you face in the book at every stage is — yourself. It permits separation of creation and criticism. It permits "sleeping on a problem," so that the results of the unconscious thinking celebrated by Poincaré and Hadamard can be added systematically to the formal thinking that has gone before.

The notebook focuses attention on one problem at a time and gives it the profit of consecutive reasoning. Usually our attention is spread fractionally over several problems so that the engine is not really coupled to any of them, or it is coupled to one and then another inconclusively several times between the first mail delivery and the coffee break. To focus attention closely, requires a certain preparation so as to have freedom from interruption, but a subway fare is enough to buy this much freedom. A man who wants to be creative will see that he has his private hour for it, and his time with the notebook will be the first duty — and pleasure — of every day, far more important than the most urgent appointments or letters. This is the first thing that must be put first; and the rewards from the pleasure and success of formal thinking can then make the rest come easily.

HUMAN FEEDBACK

Yet it is easy to see that, even when the notebook work is being done regularly, the motivation will soon grow cold without a human feedback also, a collaborator or a technical audience or the larger audience of society. Someone has said that the greatest thinking device in the world is inside a single skull: its communications channels are the most free and instantaneous. This is true as regards the ability to think, false as regards the motivation. It is the intensity and stability of our personal coupling mechanisms to other people that keep our interest alive.

One of the most important devices for coaxing the analytical mind to work is the collaborator, or perhaps two of them. The advantage is the same as that of several engines on an airplane; the lapse of one ceases to be fatal. I am not thinking here so much of the research team with its more or less interchangeable members, which is the standard arrangement now for making progress steady, as of having a second most particular sympathetic and challenging intelligence to share the thinking. Many men cannot think well unless a second is present as a mirror for their thoughts, a Doctor Watson or a protégé to admire the beautiful reasoning. I suspect there is always a second. Every poem is written to a lover and every essay to a friend. If the second is present and interacting, too, adding his own new viewpoints, so much the better.

But when the experiences and the intelligences of two persons are closely matched, this intellectual interaction can sometimes acquire a much higher intensity, a long-term friendly competition and mental stimulation which is both game and companionship, analyzing the roadblocks of thought and lifting the symbolic level at an incredible rate. I think the mountain-climbing analogy is still pertinent: with equally competent partners, both safety and speed are increased by climbing together. To be most effective, the collaborators must interact daily, it seems, and frequently must play together as well as work together (goodbye, Family) in order to keep the channels of communication free and easy and unblocked by offense or divergence or third-party intrusion. Some of the great theoretical "powerhouses" of our time have been teams of young men, Watson and Crick, Yang and Lee, Feynman and Gell-Mann, who strike intellectual sparks from each other, with minds so closely intermeshing that it is hard even for those close by to say where one mind takes over and the other leaves off. This is a powerful kind of collaboration little known in the hierarchical pyramids of the European academic tradition; but the minds of the Curies seem to have worked together like this, and Marx and Engels, and John Stuart Mill and Harriet Taylor.

Another self-reinforcing motivation for creative output is offered by the technical audience. "It takes two to speak the truth — one to speak, and another to hear." Without the approval of the boss, the tangible appreciation of the company, the name in print and the attention and response of the Society, the most eager creator can lose his productivity and his balance and turn inward on himself. So the notebook method must not run too long in a vacuum but must be converted every few months into those larger units for public presentation, the paper or the speech. The anticipation of the sea of faces, even if many of them will not be expected to understand, is a real stimulus to the organization of thought. They symbolize a spreading audience that we eventually hope to reach. Our vanity and combativeness also turn the challenge of public disagreement into a strong stimulus to think hard again. The more responsive and critical the audience, and the more direct the interaction with competitors, the stronger is the stimulus to harder thought for the next speech or paper. Many of the scientists with the strongest drive are those who were encouraged by a perceptive teacher to publish something, no matter what, at a very early age. It forces a man to elaborate and defend himself. It gets in the blood.

THE DEEP MOTIVATIONS

There is also an interaction between the creative man and a wider audience, larger and more diffuse than the technical audience. But this interaction is connected with the nature of the biological feedbacks that drive the creative process, and we need to discuss these first. Creative men are men, too. They are gregarious biological creatures and need a biological response from their fellow-creatures to complete the chain of satisfaction that keeps the analytical mind operating pleasurably. What is done, is done for them. You can see this dramatically at the great moments. The sober Cockcroft, like Archimedes, could not help running through the streets of Cambridge telling everyone, "We've split the atom! We've split the atom!" Pasteur's stimulation from successive audiences and clients and cases was a major overt motivational factor throughout his life. We have evolved our great brains in the service of primitive, selfish, fleshly physiological rewards. The mind wallows in indecision when the body or the group of bodies ceases to demand urgent smart solution. This is why the tactics of our social organization, dealing with the immediate satisfactions of money or success or victory in war, is so superb; and why the strategy, the long-range programs of human betterment or the goal of peace, is so ill-motivated and badly done. We have come up in a fierce world, and threats arouse us more than hope. I. A. Richards says, "Man is not in any sense primarily an intelligence; he is a system of interests. Intelligence helps man but does not run him."

The secret of creative output for an individual or a group is to keep the biological springs of interest flowing, so as to reward every creative act. The intelligence will then be well watered and will send forth its loveliest flowers. The secret of success in almost any personal or social problem is, Never cut off the feedback. Our individual and collective feedbacks for intellectual creation have been haphazard until now, with creation admitted grudgingly or late, or ignored where it is not actually thwarted. Acknowledgment has been mixed up with competition. Newton did not publish for Leibnitz, he published for Halley. (But good labs are now getting separate acknowledgment men, such as research directors.) The difference in scientific achievement between different laboratories and different countries lies in the perceptiveness and soundness, and the speed and thoroughness, of their acknowledgment-and-reward systems. Give an intelligent man a reward system to manipulate and he can move the world. Creation has been a flower in a dry country, eaten by animals between occasional rains. But when the principle of feedback is widely appreciated, it will be planted on an irrigation project, stretching green for miles. I speak soberly when I speak of possible order-of-magnitude increases in output, both individually and collectively.

THE POWER OF FEEDBACK

In fact one can scarcely contemplate the vistas of possible achievement from feedback, without beginning to worry about motivation going too far. It is so easy. Our greatest difficulty may finally be that of keeping individual and collective motivation balanced and sensitive to changing larger needs, not all poured into one particular rigid direction (rockets?) because of the terrific pay-off in that area. Nothing is more absurd and vicious than the mind that goes driving ahead on a single track in spite of all appeals to reason and sense, long after that goal, perhaps initially good, has become irrelevant or bad. The finest tactical mind needs to ask from time to time the question whether his work is still strategically important; unfortunately, many scientists do not. Pursuing intellect, we neglect sex; and the celibate dons die out. Pursuing social stability, we neglect the need for change. Organizations tend to amplify allegiance, and that is how we fight successful war or conduct sales campaigns; but this tendency finally makes them swollen and rigid, and an intelligent society will need to re-examine and demotivate them from time to time. The man with his notebook and the society with its feedbacks must always remember one thing: The reason why we have brains is that survival is not to be won indefinitely by any formula; that route is for insects.

But these various biological feedback principles are at the opposite pole from the way in which some self-improvers approach their problems. Some men suppose that they can *drive* their minds to think, by renouncing non-intellectual distractions, or getting better organized, or by setting schedules more precisely, or by telling themselves over and over, I've got to think, I've got to think. This is absurd. It is not by renunciation of the rest of the organism that the highest intelligence is brought forth, but by coaxing the rest of the organism to flatter and coax in turn and to *need* the kind of intelligence we want to bring forth. As Richards says again, "People who are always winning victories over themselves might equally well be described as always enslaving themselves. Their lives become unnecessarily narrow. The minds of many saints have been like wells; they should have been like lakes or like the sea."

I think this may be the real secret of the release of creative power in the great self-examinations — the integration of the whole organism around a single intellectual purpose after it has decided what its real aims are. The minds of such men as Newton or Kelvin or Pasteur or Fermi were like the sea. They were not tearing themselves away from something, they were uniting themselves toward something. The whole organism was cooperating in the result. Any man can learn this lesson.

Once we are coasting down the biological motivational hill, creation is easy. When the interest is there, and the work and the applause that keeps interest vigorous, the intellect begins to do its job at all sorts of odd times, even while we sleep or listen to music. Hadamard's *Psychology of Invention in the Mathematical Field* gives a number of such instances. I have an Austrian friend who gives this explanation of the Hungarian genius in theoretical subjects:

A Hungarian knows something about being smart that Americans do not know, that if you organize your life too tightly you cut yourself off from some ideas you might have had. A Hungarian loves music, with women and wine as an accompaniment. He relaxes, he enjoys himself, and the ideas come tip-toeing up to him of their own free will!

On an expense account, of course. Research directors, take note.

Once we understand the multiple-feedback biological integration of the individual toward his calling, we can begin to understand his relationship toward that larger audience I spoke of. There is an ultimate audience which is more than self-fulfillment and more than the lecture hall; unless a man can feel that he is communicating with it, these are ashes. I know that this ultimate audience is in many ways a myth and that even some creative men will call themselves realists and disclaim it, however irrationally they may reach for it. The poet wants his result to be immortal; but what this means in the flat facts of everyday is thirty years later some speeches in Stockholm, and a hundred years later a grubby historian's grubby little article, and two hundred years later some tangential service to the self-identification of some student in ambition or love, a misconstruction long past the artist's satisfaction or control. I doubt if the highest flights of the human intellect are really flown for this. When we talk of real goods, Eureka! is its own reward, and the best one. Yet I also doubt if much science would get done for the moments of discovery alone. The ultimate audience for which the scientist works is no more real than the ultimate audience for which the captain goes down with his ship or for which the dog is faithful to the end; but it is just as compelling. It is a symbol of mammalian group survival, and it is exactly in the moments of the greatest crisis or the highest achievement that these other-directed symbols win out over individual and physiological goods and "realities." The group immortality is the real immortality; and the group must honor these symbols and keep them green for the creator and the sacrificer, or it really dies. The group must use and appreciate, and it must keep alive in the artist the notion that he is creating an immortal result. To keep intellectual creation flowing, some good fraction of a man's most significant thought must be carried through to some kind of permanent public effect or response, a credit line or a tangible product, that he can point to and take pride in because it seems to reach this ultimate audience.

REACHING AN AUDIENCE

It is not always easy to get this kind of acknowledgement. The organizations that might have supported a creator in this purpose often stand in the way of his public fulfillment. As one observer has put it:

> A scientist or an engineer . . . discovers that the Organization cannot tolerate a large output of new ideas. Either there is insufficient capital to take advantage of them, or too great a risk to current operations, or too little experience with exploitation procedures, or any of a number of other reasons . . . The Organization in America is also exceedingly efficient at burying ideas, saving out only a small fraction for keeping up with the competition. Thus it is not surprising that a large fraction of the non-university scientists and engineers are bitter. As compared to all other professions, their morale is the lowest.

Yet it is also true that many abstractly creative people do not think their ideas all the way through to public effect and fulfillment. They do not concentrate on ideas of maximum effect and do not consider analytically the sequence of steps necessary for a permanent result and how the sequence could be made automatic, with each step "giving a prize." They may think that their work ends with the company memorandum or publication and that it only remains for lesser men to see the light and take up their great ideas. To cite Fermi's case once more, one of the characteristics that made his work so effective was his insistence on trying every step of even a large group experiment with his own hands, turning his analytical reasoning toward optimizing every element and checking for hidden bottlenecks, using brute force on a calculation here or machining out a mechanical part there, so as to get the fastest operational effectiveness without waiting for the elegance of the drafting room or the professional mathematician.

This same attitude must be applied to the sequential details of reaching an audience or creating a social result. L. R. Hafstad has spoken of the necessity of having an "impedance match" in transmitting understanding to an audience just as in transmitting power from a power source to an operating system. On the one hand, the effectiveness is low if the audience is too easily moved, because it does not really absorb the communication and will be as easily moved by some competing source. On the other hand, if the audience is too stubborn, the communication passes by with no effect. Maximum effectiveness results from finding a maximally effective audience (or communication channel to them) and putting in the right kind of appeal backed by the right kind of power to move them. It costs the mover some effort too! — but it is worth it. As someone has said somewhere, it is harder to carve wood than cheese, but no sculptor would use cheese. Some of the finest brains I know are spinning in a vacuum, to the loss of all of us, because they have never paid the necessary attention to explaining and disseminating their ideas and persuading an audience; that is, to *coupling* their ideas to human activity for maximum effectiveness.

GROUP OUTPUT

Finally I want to touch on some additional factors that come into play in determining the creative output of large groups and whole societies. Most of the factors in a good research team are fairly obvious generalizations of the factors for individuals. Every good research director knows the needs of analytical and creative minds for empathy, flattery, challenge, free communication and mutual dependence, with a minimum of internal blocks such as are caused by competition in rank or services; for information on the fate of their ideas; and for protection from trivial intrusion in their hours of reasoning. A research team is an amplifying device, not an accounting office. Inadequate secretaries or forms in quintuplicate may save thousands and cost millions. A clumsy research director may wreck the group output just by moving a desk, if it changes the personal intellectual coupling between his best men.

In an educational research group, there are other important factors. One of my colleagues says his hardest problem is to transfer an idea to a student so subtly that the student will think he thought of it himself. This makes him cocky and independent, and by and by he begins to create his own. The success of G. N. Lewis' School of Chemistry at Berkeley, which produced about half the top-notch senior physical chemists in America today, seems to have been due in large measure to the systematic use of various motivational devices to make the students eager to learn and to succeed.

Further factors come in when we consider the creative output of a whole society. There are nonretentive societies — and fields of work — and retentive ones. The nonretentive society is a Sisyphus society, where every generation must start over again from the bottom, with no new symbolic apparatus or short cuts to speed its ascent. Society's achievement is just the best man's achievement, perhaps a few gamesworth of formal application a year for a dozen years. Art is such a field, and every new sculptor must do over again many of the same gamesworth that Praxiteles did, with almost no new shortcuts to speed his learning.

But after three hundred competitive years of a retentive society such as Western culture, or of a field such as science, the level of difficulty of the problems that can be solved may represent the concentrated and accumulated work of that whole time, perhaps some tens of thousands of gamesworth of analysis beyond untrained perception, in several fields. I do not think our individual brains today can think up preciably faster or more accurately than those of primitive men. Our achievements are due to two factors, the first of which is that the constant leakage has stopped. Sisyphus has climbed out of Hades.

CREATIVE EDUCATION

They are due, secondly, to the fact that the children can be brought up by a symbolic cable car so that they can start where their fathers left off. Tens of thousands of games-worth are too much to teach a child, but when the regularities of that problem-solving are codified into symbols, these short cuts permit him to learn in a few weeks what took a century to establish. A fifteen-year-old can learn the Periodic Table summarizing thousands of man-years of chemistry. The first leg of progress is retention; the second is compression in learning — that is to say, symbols and schools.

It is commonly lamented today that a man cannot know everything, as he could in Bacon's time, or Franklin's. I think he could, if we could invent more rapid symbolic compression, or practice more effectively what we now have. Consider the schools. Up to age fifteen, a child learns little more, and little more rapidly, than he might have learned in the time of Descartes, except perhaps for a few subjects, astronomy, geography, and some biology. Then suddenly, after his time of fastest learning is past, we try to compress into him in six or eight years all that we can of the last three hundred. This is like stuffing the top of the trunk after the lower section has been badly packed. No wonder it will not all fit.

If we thought seriously about how to spread this burden down into the lower grades and into the homes, and how to make more symbolic compression of the traditional material, it might be different. Children cannot understand human relations until their gonads start to work, but the child of six now knows the germ theory. At nine to twelve he could be learning substantial and accurate amounts of the principles of modern physics, chemistry, biology and medicine, mathematical logic, feedback and servo systems and game theory, to name a few — if we would only take the trouble to use our advanced knowledge to describe in a simple language the numerous simple practical demonstrations of these principles that lie everywhere at hand. If we went on to apply also what we know now about continuous incentives and learning speeds, we could turn out vastly broader and more knowledgeable adults than we do now.

It is a commonplace to say that compression in learning has always led to great increases in intellectual achievement. Yet few persons appreciate how closely the major achievements in many fields have been connected with the appearance of schools — creative schools, I mean, teaching technique and short cuts, not the schools of scholars. It was the setting up of schools of philosophy where a succession of the young — Socrates, Plato, Aristotle — could find a technique, an interest and an audience, that made the Greeks advance so fast in that area. More recent philosophical advances have come tangentially out of the vigorously creative schools of other subjects, psychology, mathematical logic, or physics.

It was the appearance of creative schools of art that made the Italians and Dutch advance so fast there. It has been the creative schools of science that have made the West advance so fast in that field. We can easily see the social feedbacks that make these schools appear and flourish: rich men's sons for the philosophers to lecture to, rich and educated dukes and burghers to patronize the artists, rich dukes and then industries and governments to buy science. Let the buying caste decline, and the schools and the achievements fade away.

The thing that has made the academic humanities so neglected in our time — as contrasted with the commercial creative humanities, which are flourishing — is their almost complete divorce from creative training of the young by creators. Of four great men in four different fields, Newton, Michelangelo, Shakespeare, and Mozart, the only one who could be a full-time faculty member at a major university today is Newton. The others would have to go to some less ingrown social institutions if they wished to found schools or to find a fully rewarding audience. I think that whatever unbalance there is in our society between technology and the humanities, as lamented so often by the academic humanists, can be corrected as soon as they begin to think about, and to create around them, the conditions for continuously flourishing schools of creative output.

But in every direction I think there lie before us vistas of creative achievement and personal satisfaction in our work such as we have never dreamed of before.

9. SCIENTIFIC KNOWLEDGE
AND SOCIAL VALUES

WHAT IS the moral responsibility of the scientist?

This is a question frequently addressed to the physical scientist today by students and ministers and novelists and other moralists. What a loaded question it is! At times the nuclear physicist must feel that the whole conscience of the world is leveled at him.

Public opinion can be a cleft stick. If you work on The Bomb, you are an enemy of humanity; if you refuse, you are lacking in national enthusiasm. If it were not for the honor of the thing — as the man said who was being ridden out of town on a rail — the physicist would prefer to be excused from this double bind. He would like to see the question of moral responsibility reflected back to the soldier and the editorialist and to the boards of directors and legislators and citizens who are so busy hiring him to make their bombs and missiles.

Nevertheless there is no doubt that the question of the scientist's moral responsibility is a central one. It is science and technology that have provided the powder and fuse for today's explosive world. We are all shaken by this. Many a scientist, like many a citizen, has lost his whole faith in the goodness of science. One is reminded of the myths of Faust and Frankenstein and one wonders if there is actually, as the poets have said, some malignant tendency attached to our impious efforts to pry out the secrets of nature. Is science deeply in the service of human values, or not? And if not, why not?

THE GREAT CONTRADICTION

The current contradiction between the ideals and some of the results of science is clear enough. For centuries now, scientists have pleaded that they had a new and special morality, a conscientious obligation to pursue truth alone at all costs whenever anybody wanted them to do anything else. Freedom of inquiry! Detachment! Knowledge for itself! These were the rules that would free men from the grip of religious dogma and narrow profit-seeking and would lead them to the larger control over nature and the larger human good. Ye shall know the truth and the truth shall make you free, we all have said, thinking somehow that this now applies to the truths of science as well as to the truth of life.

This has been a great ideal and a great faith and it has brought us magnificent technological rewards. The difficulty is that, from Hiroshima on, the most fundamental of sciences seems to have brought some horrible and terrifying rewards as well. All at once, the morality of the pure pursuit of objective truth seems to have run colossally afoul of the grand old morality of respect for life, just as the humane men so often predicted it would. Basic scientists have had to face the fact that nuclear weapons were actually made possible by the most basic and pure and detached of studies and that the blame could not be pushed off onto engineers and technologists and practical men, as it could be earlier with dynamite or the machine gun.

As a result, their faith in detachment has almost van-

ished. Many physical scientists have become sick at heart.
Some have joined the church again, some have abandoned
nuclear science, some have said they would study butterfly
wings rather than go back to secret projects. Today the
students are arrayed hotly for and against science, trying
to argue down their own uncertainties. And many leading
physicists and chemists have turned to vigorous political
and international action of various kinds, hoping they can
find some plan that will still rescue the situation and keep
us all from being finished off in the next spasm of alarm.
Whether you agree with them or not, they are certainly
men driven by a moral imperative to action and by a depth
of conviction such as most of us have rarely seen.

Did we really think beforehand that things would be different? All knowledge is dangerous until we learn to handle
it. It was so from the beginning, with fire and the knife.
In fact the dangers of the new weapons that we know today, physical weapons and chemical weapons and biological
warfare, may be as nothing compared to the dangers that
lie ahead, when the psychological and social sciences come
of age. At least one well-known psychologist has said
privately,

Psychology is actually a far more dangerous study than
physics. Every real operational advance in psychology has
led to a further erosion of human independence and freedom. Galton's measurements on human physiques led to
Bertillon's system of criminal identification. Pavlov's con-
ditioned reflexes led to methods for the brainwashing of
prisoners. Psychoelectrical studies led to the lie detector.
Psychochemistry, to truth drugs. Intelligence tests, to the
security questionnaire and the company questionnaire.
Studies on the thresholds of perception, to subliminal ad-

vertising. And we are just at the beginning. Some of the new conditioning methods are a hundred times more effective. It is not individual welfare but the welfare of commercial organizations and governments and dictators that profits most from new psychological knowledge.

This is a one-sided view, no doubt. But think what still more absolute and effortless methods of control the social sciences may give us if they ever become operational sciences, too!

Must knowledge always bring, along with its unmistakable blessings, these terrifying threats to life and to the human spirit? Must the scientist now give up completely his Baconian optimism about the human value of his work? Must he always feel guilty of releasing a monster that can make no distinction between good and bad ends?

I think not. The dangers that threaten the human spirit in some applications or misapplications of increased knowledge and control should never be minimized. The moral responsibility for every encroachment that threatens should be a matter of continual concern to both scientists and citizens. Nevertheless, I think that the real origin of our collective difficulties lies elsewhere. It has been so easy and instinctive to blame science and to blame the scientists for our troubles, as they have blamed themselves, that we have been kept from looking deeper at the details of the process by which science produces its good or bad results. I think that when we do look, we will see that there is a big difference between the situations where it brings good and those where it brings bad. The difference is that in the one case we have clarity and unanimity in our human purposes and in the other case we have confusion and conflict.

It is not our acquisition of knowledge that is dangerous,

but our failure to know and to agree on the ends we want to put it to. Whenever the values of individual integrity collide with the values of the social organization, or whenever the purposes of one group or nation collide with those of another, greater scientific knowledge only makes the collisions more catastrophic. But when certain primary goods, such as the mutual increase of health or wealth or survival, are clear and are the same for all parties, as I think in some of our major problems they can be and will be, the contributions of scientific knowledge toward the solution are clear also, and the blessings of knowledge become unmixed blessings. We use the truth we know to get the good we think we want. When the good is clear, the value of the truth is clear also.

Let us look at a few situations where what is good is clear and where it is unclear, and see how this principle of undivided purposes works and how it helps our understanding of the human value of science and of the responsibilities of the scientist in such cases.

WHEN THE GOOD IS CLEAR

Let us consider first how men acquire and use knowledge in situations where what is good is absolutely unambiguous. In society this is rare, but when a man is stranded on a desert island or in the wilderness, he finds that he does have a central purpose and that it is very clear. It is to stay alive and intact. His need sharpens his mind wonderfully. He rediscovers the facts built into every cell of his body, that for ten million generations we have survived by the skin of our teeth and we survivors are a fierce and special breed, focused on survival. He rediscovers that he is a unitary biological creature, an individual — "undivided" — with one complete set of biological needs and purposes, one nervous network to gather information and to make decisions, and one muscular system guided by these decisions to act to satisfy these needs. All his parts and purposes become subclauses in the paragraph of survival.

As a result, the need for objective knowledge and the proper uses of knowledge and the value of knowledge all become very clear to the castaway. Knowledge is to be related to purposes, decisions, and acts. This man wants a survival manual, not a treatise on quantum mechanics. He wants to know the look of the sky before a storm, how to make bird lures, what mushrooms are edible, and how to make a bow or build a boat. If he has no book and must learn these things all over again for himself, why, that is what his vision and his other senses and his hunches and invention are for, as they were the first time these things were discovered. They are for the pursuit of objective truth. The castaway becomes a scientist of survival and would laugh at the suggestion that too much objective knowledge could be bad for him. He would know what parts to pick out. *Robinson Crusoe* is one long study of the proper application of objective knowledge to individual human purposes.

Is there any danger that this isolated man will pursue truth for bad ends or will conduct irrational experiments that contradict his biological purposes? This is possible, let us face it. He may torture his dog for amusement. He may finally go mad and cut off his hand. But generally the stranded airman still hoping for rescue is not interested in slicing himself to measure his blood flow or the sensation of pain; he fears he will come to that soon enough anyway.

One of his hands does not fight the other; he is busy using them to catch game and birds and fish. The biochemists tell us, it is true, that the desperate starving body consumes certain of its own cells biochemically before it consumes others, but they emphasize that it saves as long as possible the central and integral structures from which all the rest can be rejuvenated again.

And the man on the island teaches us a lot about science. We do not always keep in mind the essential fact that it is man the wanter, man the user, that knowledge is for. In science, demonstrable truth is often called "operational" truth, meaning the kind of truth clear enough to predict the observable results of a reproducible operation. "Take one gram of potassium metal and drop it on water and it will catch fire," says the book, and it is true. Scientific instruction is always at least implicitly of the form, "*If* I do this, *then* that will happen." It is in two parts, not one. "If I do this" is the operation, what I may will; "then that will happen" is the result, what is determined. The determinate part is not good or bad, it is just true. Or if it is good, its goodness is just that of objective truth, which can be used by any man, good or bad, for his own purposes.

But what the book omits to emphasize, and what we forget, is that in these operational prescriptions of science, man is the operator, the one who wills. Me. You. Many of the debates over determinism and free will have missed this double structure of science. The experimenter, man, is the fierce piece of protoplasm who stands outside the predictions of this external world. He is the one who has desires and purposes, who decides and acts, who "takes" the gram and "drops" it, who watches and uses, who wants or doesn't want the result, and who does or doesn't do the opcration. In science, the external consequences are determined; but it is the internal man who wants and knows and decides and wills and acts. This is very old and very obvious; and yet we often need to be reminded of it in discussing the relation of science to man.

KNOWLEDGE FOR A WORLD SOCIETY

In this light, consider what science would do in a society that is clear about its purposes. There is no such animal, you say? Well, I am an optimist; and I think that there is, or will be soon, some kind of world society where the primary goods are almost as clear and unanimous as they are to the stranded airman. If we survive at all, it cannot be long before this earth — our own little island in a sea of space — contains a single interconnected human race. I am not sure whether this will be under one government, or under many, holding their mutual threats in check somehow; such governmental structures and controls might well evolve back and forth over the years from one form to another. But if we survive, we will certainly have to be more intimately interconnected than we are now, and our collective goods will then become very clear to us. We will necessarily be channeling our energies much less into coercing and threatening each other and much more into meeting our individual and collective needs for food and warmth, for thought and communication, and for novelty and beauty and enterprise.

In fact, once war and lethal national competition are removed, there will be little else for us to do! Right now we have sufficient technical control of our environment that we can supply our basic biological needs rather easily on this earth. If we can keep our population down, we have enough air, water, food potential, mineral resources, and atomic and solar energy for thousands or millions of years, once we have put our good Robinson Crusoe sense to work on mining and conserving and using these resources.

I believe there can be no doubt that, if we survive, our primary values must begin to be universal, not American values or Russian or Chinese values, but basic biological and psychological values growing clearer and stronger as our interconnectedness grows over the years. The value of science will then be universal, too. For suppose a world society did start out by misusing scientific knowledge for oppression. In a well-knit group, the voice of those who are oppressed will finally begin to be heard through some communications channels, and men will shudder and respond. We are all members one of another, even under the worst of states. This will produce a loss of the cohesion and efficiency of the society; and a government safe from external threats will not be able to support such a cost, and will begin to avoid and alleviate the damage to the body social, as a man avoids self-inflicted pain.

Is there starvation somewhere? Food will be rushed. Is someone enslaved or tried or shot unjustly? Is industrial work oppressive and hazardous? Are doctors experimenting with prisoners, or psychologists with subjects, beyond their free consent? The news travels like lightning and the world responds with indignation and action. One has only to list these situations to realize how nearly we have reached this state already, over most of the world. We frequently do not appreciate what an intimate connection there is between advanced communications and an advanced conscience. They make it possible, and therefore inevitable, for man the decider, man the operator, to take appropriate action.

TRUTH IN A DIVIDED WORLD

I think these special cases help us see what we want and what we ought to do in another kind of society — our own. Even in a world with partial and divided purposes, the rule of coincidence of purposes can help show to what degree science serves human values and where the blame for its ill-effects should be placed. Undoubtedly each of our little social or national groups today — each one almost as unified a decision-maker as the man on the desert island — is using scientific and technological truth to advance its own purposes. Within each of their limited frames of reference, more truth is certainly a good.

The difficulty is that the biggest of these groups today are national groups, and that their purposes are to kill each other, or at least to threaten to. "We will bury you," says one. " 'Second strike' retaliation," says the other. More scientific truth obviously enables them to threaten or to kill each other more thoroughly, and, in view of their probable collective responses and counterresponses, it is certainly an evil for all of our purposes as human beings.

In such a world, scientists differ not so much on moral values as on their estimates of the consequences. Is a trace of weed killer in the food worse? — or weeds? Is death from fall-out worse? — or the Communist/capitalist system? If we could predict the consequences more reliably, or improve them, these debates would disappear. This has happened already to many old and bitter debates such as those over the adoption of public health measures or the regulation of the stock market.

But in crucial areas where prediction or control of results is still very difficult, a scientist's view of the consequences, like any other man's, is colored by his loyalties. Intelligent men differ violently. In the international field, the consequences of any course of action are still so unpredictable that I think we must respect any man who is using his intelligence in the service of large loyalties. If a man's loyalties are to an ideal of nonviolence and he refuses to work on nuclear energy, I respect him. If his loyalties are to the survival of his nation and he works on nuclear weapons for what he thinks is a good way of life, I respect him. If his loyalties are to the human race and he works on nuclear energy or weapons for what he thinks is an eventual scientific benefit to the whole human race, I respect him. If his loyalties are to the human race and he drops his work on nuclear energy to work on political solutions to keep us all from getting killed, I respect him.

The only man I do not respect is the man who has not yet asked himself what he is working for.

Yet now the situation has in fact become so dangerous, with the world perpetually only a half hour or so away from complete annihilation, that many of these loyalties and moral positions might as well be restructured. The pacifist scientist who refuses to do research on certain supposedly wicked things is really only denying the use of his brains in that direction to the human race, for nothing he could do could hurt us any more; and it might help. Likewise, the patriotic scientist who works on secret bombs or missiles or biological warfare supposedly to protect his national way of life is no longer actually protecting it unless he is really trying at the same time to get a political control system accepted in which these things will never be used. The patriot and the pacifist, and the State Department and the Kremlin, are in fact becoming united in their basic objectives of security for each nation and for the world. In the pursuit of peace, just as elsewhere in the competition to aid underdeveloped countries and the competition to explore space, that world of common purposes that I described is still dangerously far away, but also tantalizingly close.

THE PRESSURE OF KNOWLEDGE

The purposes and programs of these diverse leaders are moving together because the purposes of the world are moving together. But is not this always the effect of scientific knowledge in a divided society? — that when we think we are using it for our own little aims, it is actually expanding the whole social objective and the whole framework of our understanding? Here we come to the true and deepest function of science, that it not only serves the purposes of man, it interacts with them and changes them. It expands the scope of the social good, and then it expands our very concept of the good, as we shall see. It is this power, pregnant and irreversible, that makes our little bloody battles obsolete.

Let us see how it changes the scope of the good. At first it seems that demonstrable truth makes it possible to pursue every goal more effectively, small or large. It amplifies the power in every human hand. The molecular knowledge of the match and the gun enlarges the criminal's power. But the demonstrable truth of electromagnetic waves becomes a radio network and enlarges the powers of the police.

And here is the real evolutionary force of factual truth. In amplifying all our powers, it does far more for our social powers than for our individual powers. Thieves can have no radio network for long. Only big companies and big nations can do research. We are new at these things and we have not yet learned to use our scientific knowledge for many of our larger public wants, but it is evident that scope will count.

Demonstrable truth is social. To find and to apply it takes a large and cohesive society; and the society becomes larger and more cohesive as a result. The little purposes of the little duchies of Europe are not as well served by science as the larger purposes of nations that span continents and form blocs. Once they said, You immoral man, whose side are you on, your family's or the enemy's? But after a generation it made little difference which of the Dukes Galileo had served. The greatest value of their pride and their wars was that it gave him and others like him an incentive for some permanent contributions to universal knowledge or the arts. These little moralities that can be blessed with equal fervor by the bishops on both sides are too small for our world. Scientists who serve governments frequently console themselves with this thought. They imagine that the governments are serving them. In rocketry, at least, they are right.

It is true that science sometimes appears to serve madness. My friend the rabbi raises his gentle eyebrows and asks, "And were the German Nazi doctors pursuing truth by giving massive overdoses to Jewish subjects?" No, and they knew it. Not all the vicious and stupid things that are done in the name of science are science, any more than the vicious and stupid things that have been done in the name of religion are religion. The German madmen were finally mad enough that they wrecked themselves.

For what is madness but the refusal to take the long-run view in the light of all the facts? In spite of the Mad Scientist figure of the comic strips, scientists are perhaps as far from insanity as anyone in the world. Madness is the negation of objective truth. The truth finally catches a man up and straightens him out, or destroys him. The Nazis who expelled the Jewish scientists gave all the aces to the enemy.

No one denies that the good and evil purposes sometimes seem to be served together. The scientific society talks and works for a good life for all individuals; and today its mistakes grow monstrous. Ignorance becomes too expensive for it, poverty anywhere becomes too dangerous for it, it sends aid to underdeveloped countries; and then it threatens the race with extinction. But if we could possibly look at this dispassionately, as from a great distance, would not all of these be parallel signs that science is serving the world purpose even better than the national purpose? With our ancient threats and counterthreats, we in our nations may still be stupid enough to annihilate ourselves; but if we survive, it will only be by finding a route to a world society at peace.

It often takes several rounds to reach these larger goals. In many social problems we are not there yet. But empirical knowledge is not like the empty debates and quibbles of the medieval schoolmen. It is effective. It jumps boundaries and undermines social systems. It is impatient with partial or temporary solutions. It gets out of hand when it is used for petty ends. Men do not use it; it uses them. It takes them up and knocks their heads together and rubs their noses in the facts. And after every round, communication is faster, horizons are larger and sympathies are wider.

One nation's good is another nation's evil. Whoever wins, a good is diminished and canceled out. One man's truth is another man's truth. It is never diminished or canceled out. Whoever wins, the truth is enlarged. When men strive for their goods, they defeat one another. When they strive for the truth, they enlarge one another. The knowledge of how to deal with our common environment and our common problems grows over history. In a world of limited and divided objectives, perhaps the enlarging truth is the greatest of the goods. In a divided world, what smaller aim is really moral?

THE GROWING IDEA OF GOOD

When we enlarge the possibility of the good, we enlarge our concept of the good also. To discuss this, we need to think clearly about what we mean by good. Speaking purely biologically, is what we call good not basically related, in every case, to survival of the race? With the first one-celled animal, every chemical or motor reaction is aimed at survival. With us, every gesture we make probably has some relation to some biological purpose, no matter how small, and anticipates a favorable return of some sort, related to survival. Even the cruelty of the psychopath satisfies some neuron somewhere in his disordered brain, no doubt. But we can see farther than a one-celled animal, and we call good only those acts that have a larger or a longer-range relation to survival, the mother's smile, the neighbor's help, or the architect's plan.

A society tries to survive, too. Every society has had its

rules of structure and rules of order and personal and group decision rules that held it together, or didn't, in times of stress. Anthropologically speaking, in any society that has survived, the rules that happened to survive with it are what that society calls moral. Polygamy. Monogamy. No murder within the society, but theft and murder blessed against foreigners. What is good depends on the time, the place and the enemy. But we can now see farther than a single society. We find a truth that is certainly indifferent to ends as special as these.

(There are some high religious values, of course, that are not merely matters of obvious self-interest. Self-sacrifice, for example. That of the mother for the child or the soldier for his buddy is so instinctive and irresistible in moments of crisis that it proves we have grown up in families and tribes and have survived only by being willing to dare for each other. We see why we are members one of another. And we have faith in the ultimate value of acts of love and mercy even when all the consequences are not foreseeable. Even in cold blood, we have surprising instincts of charity. It has been reported that five-sixths of all American soldiers will not fire directly at enemy soldiers in battle. [So those who want more killing power want push-button weapons, which permit fewer men to produce greater consequences with less conscience.] Science can add nothing to these moralities of faith. It announces its uncertainty from the beginning, and it cannot predict the infinitely distant consequences any better than the saint.)

What science does do for morality is to enlarge it by showing it how to obtain the practical goods of health and survival, the foreseeable goods, more widely and easily and accurately, and by uniting it into societies that pursue these goods more successfully. In human society, there are not only competing goods, there are different levels of good, that of the individual, the family, the business organization, the nation, or the human race. Society finds that few of us can afford much long-range good, and so it must find ways of turning its eventual higher-level goods into our individual daily rewards so as to get its larger projects done. We pay the postman and the teacher for services that were once done out of the goodness of someone's heart and we get better mail service and better education as a result. Society is organization for our goods. When we can see farther and turn these long-range goods into short-range goods more reliably, the larger good is made more attainable, and our ideas of what is good are made larger too.

Good is natural to men. But it grows by being made possible. It is a common belief among humanists and moralists and those who have alienated themselves from science that science and technology have never brought us anything but material goods. This is a blindness, I believe. Consumer goods are the least of their gifts. Goods and power and knowledge were only the preconditions for the abolition of dogma and feudalism and slavery, for the increase of human welfare and hope, for the enlargement of our horizons and our communications and our sympathies, and for the growth of our responsibility as masters of our own earth and our humility as children of the cosmos. Are not these goods of the spirit? Is it science, or our own limitations, that have made some of its gifts less inspiring?

We have always known, really, that virtue and goodwill are not enough, and that real goodness demands the widest possible understanding. Job, that good man, in his suffering says, Show me my guilt! But what God shows him instead is his ignorance, his ignorance and helplessness before the great natural forces of the world. It was the first Ph.D. examination, as Harlow Shapley once said; and the candidate failed. I think that in this enigmatic story there is a prophetic point that is often missed. The message of Job is that we should be humble before the ruthless magnificence of the universe. We should admire and accept it because we are all so small and sinful and life is so short. But at the end I think the book may also be suggesting that we will someday use the minds we were given to look nature in the face and to help ourselves as much as we can. It is when man searches out the foundations of the earth and how the horse and Leviathan were made that he begins to be able to avoid some of his catastrophes and plagues. In the end the cure for human suffering and helplessness is not suppliance or acceptance but science.

KNOWLEDGE AND GROWTH

We see that science is somewhat like rain; it not only nourishes our purposes, it enlarges them. It will bestow its fullest benefits only on a biological organism, an individual or a nation or a world, that has finally become unitary and unmistakable about its purposes. An undivided one who knows the great Truths, the truths of life — what his basic goods really are and what the relation is between his knowledge, his purposes and his acts — will get nothing but good from the scientific and objective truths he uses.

To say it another way, many of our social stresses in the present time of unfamiliar challenges and conflicting purposes are the growing pains of men whose horizons are widening. We could not avoid the pains without giving up the horizons. But we are still adolescents and we blame the food.

The scientist today evidently needs to be clear in his own mind about what group and what good he is really working for. Beyond that, it seems to me that the moral responsibility of the scientist is just the same as that of a man with a family in any other desperate situation. It is to use his head. The only things that can increase our danger now are stupidity or accident, and any contribution of intelligence can only improve the situation. The worst wickedness is stupidity, the stupidity of smallness or carelessness, of using less than our highest intelligence; and perhaps it has always been. In this sense, we have enough morality and good-will; it is brains we need.

In particular, it seems to me that the problem of obtaining security and human satisfactions in those areas where science and advancing technology have given very dubious blessings is no more a moral problem than the organization of a city government in a frontier town is a moral problem. Both of them are technical social problems first of all, not to be solved by renunciation or by indignation meetings or by buying the sheriff bigger pistols, but only by making a workable social organization.

Science cannot be put back into the bottle, for it is another step in evolution. The human race may be annihilated, but it cannot be put back into duchies. We are like a boy learning to drive a car. He may kill himself, but he is determined to learn. There is no responsibility without decision, and no decision without the danger of a wrong one. Do we really want to be protected from our choices by some providential Hand? Do we really think we would make any better decisions if they came on us more slowly?

Scientific knowledge has made possible the car. Let us think and plan as hard as we can; but the only way to learn to drive is to drive.

The intellect is not all of a man or even the primary part. We have dreams and desires and fears; we want to love and laugh and enjoy and pursue the beautiful and be aware. Science, which is the intellect of mankind, is not all of the life of mankind. But just as it enlarges the individual scientist, so it is enlarging us all and knitting us all together so that we can pursue our other objectives more effectively. This is not merely the service of knowledge, but the service of wisdom, of Truth with a capital T.

A man may be narrow and petty, but if he once accepts the scientific test of truth, the test of objective and reproducible and interrelated fact, he has opened his mind to correction and growth. Even his pettiness begins to be used to interact with and to correct the excesses of others and to contribute to the collective establishment of knowledge. Scientists today interact with each other so much that they begin to think of themselves as cells in a collective mind, thinking and criticizing and creating together. If one drops out, another takes his place. What is done is done by many at once and indeed is done by all. American and Russian, British and German, Hungarian and Japanese, whether they are allowed to talk to each other or not, their results move together and all their ideas contribute in the end.

The collective mind is moving toward one truth, one planet, and one enterprise. It is the mind of man the operator, man the decider, beginning to operate for man's purposes with all the truth he knows. It is leading us toward the highest good we know as men, the fullest development of the powers and responsibilities of the whole human race.

Is the pursuit of scientific truth immoral? Can more knowledge be hurtful? It is only small purposes that are immoral or hurtful. The truth is to the good as the tool is to the hand. The tool is an extension of the hand. The hand will not cut itself. Shall not the hand then reach for truth?